SWORD STUDY

Parent Edition

Written by
Tammy McMahan

Illustrations by
Doug McGuire

Vignettes by·
Marti Pieper

Sword Study
Parent Edition

2013 SWORD STUDY, Parent Edition
Copyright © 2013 The Shelby Kennedy Foundation
Published by The Shelby Kennedy Foundation
First printing June 2013

Editor, Jill Morris
Design Manager, Caroline McKenzie

ISBN: 978-1-939966-05-6

Dewey Decimal Classification Number: 227

Scripture quotations identified KJV are taken from the King James Version.

Scripture quotations identified NKJV are taken from the New King James Version. Copyright © 1982 by Thomas Nelson, Inc. Used by permission. All rights reserved.

Scripture quotations identified NASB are taken from the The Holy Bible, NEW AMERICAN STANDARD VERSION. Copyright © 1960, 1962, 1968, 1971, 1972, 1973, 1975, 1977, 1995 by The Lockman Foundation. Used by permission. All rights reserved.

Scripture quotations identified NIV are taken from the HOLY BIBLE, NEW INTERNATIONAL VERSION. Copyright © 1973, 1978, 1984 by the International Bible Society. Used by permission of International Bible Society. All rights reserved.

Scripture quotations identified ESV are taken from The English Standard Version. Copyright © 1993, 1994, 1995, 1996, 2000, 2001, 2002. Used by permission, Crossway Division of Good News Publishers. All rights reserved.

Word Study Part A entries based on Strong's Exhaustive Concordance of the Bible and Greek Dictionary of the New Testament. Word Study Part B entries are based on Vine's Concise Dictionary of the Bible, and Zodhiate's Complete Word Study Dictionary: New Testament.

Printed in the United States of America.

For more information about resources for studying the Bible together as a family, or to order additional copies of this resource, visit www.biblebee.org

DEDICATION

*To the glory and honor of
my Heavenly Father.*

To my husband Mark, my faithful, loving friend and rock.

*To my dear parents, for your faithful example
of walking in the light and abiding in the Word,
and encouraging me to carry on. To my strong sons of the Light,*

*Alex, Zachary and Hunter:
May you study His Word so that you **know** Him, and share His
knowledge! I love you all dearly.*

~ ACKNOWLEDGEMENTS ~

*To... Mom, Caroline, Jill and Susan: you are such a gift as fellow racers.
What an amazing, invigorating, stretching race! Only our Lord knows the details
of the race He set before us. Praise Him for the strength, love, grace and
fellowship that He provided to me through your partnerships. You are the best
fellow racers a friend could ask for... ever! Love you dearly!*

*To... My dearest prayer warriors and friends: you are mighty, faithful and
enduring. How obviously supernatural to feel your prayers from all
corners of the country and feel as though we have fellowshipped over this
book together. Praise our Lord for His provision of YOU! Love you dearly!*

*To... Our diligent reviewers, Becky, Dana, Hunter, Kelsey, Kristen, Kristi,
Nicole, Teresa and Tom: may the Lord bless you for your refining words,
efforts and encouragement. Love you dearly!*

SECTIONS

SWORD STUDY OVERVIEW

SUMMARY
What to Expect each Week

SWORD STUDY

An in-depth study of 1 John for 5 days each week. The daily study will consist of devotion, investigation of the Scriptures, and guided prayer following the A.C.T.S. model.
Time: approximately 20 minutes

A.C.T.S. PRAYER

A time set aside daily to speak directly to the Lord and write to Him using the A.C.T.S. acrostic prayer model.

FAMILY BONFIRE

A planned gathering time designated for family review and discussion centered around the weekly Sword Study lessons and the unique Bible Bee "Day 10 Diagrams".
Time and day to be determined by family.

BIBLE MEMORY PASSAGES

All family members will be encouraged to memorize the same Bible Memory passages each week. The passages beautifully correspond to what is being studied in the Sword Study. Bible Memory Cards are included at the back of the Parent Guidebook for ease of learning for parents and Young Explorers.

WEEK AT A GLANCE

Weekly

AN INTRODUCTORY STORY

The first day of each week will begin with a vignette. It is designed to be a prelude to the main themes that you will be studying during the week.

FIVE DAYS OF STUDY

Students will be led through five days of study each week. Each book's chapter will be studied over a two-week period, starting with an overview of the chapter and then moving through the Investigative Study to a final "Day 10 Diagram" summary of the entire chapter at the end of the two-week period.

Daily

ON YOUR KNEES: PRAY, WRITE, READ

Students will begin each day by praying for a quiet and focused heart. Then, they will write out verses to create their own copy of Scripture in the WRITE! tab and read through the book.

INVESTIGATIVE STUDY: 1-2-3

Students will be led through simple steps of the Investigative Study by allowing Scripture to answer Scripture.

APPLY!

At the closing of certain days of study, students will apply what they have learned that day. Some days, students are given optional "Digging Deeper" activities to increase their knowledge and understanding.

Continued on next page...

WEEK AT A GLANCE

Daily

A.C.T.S. PRAYER

Each day will conclude with a guided prayer time to help students think through the Scriptures they investigated in their study. Initially, we will help them pray through each step of the A.C.T.S. prayer model. After the first week, we encourage the writing of personal prayers within the Sword Study .

A - Adoration

In Adoration we will worship God for who He is and what He has done. We will focus on His character, attributes, and/or deeds that we saw in His Word that day.

C - Confession

In our time of Confession we will focus on our sin. We will take God's Word, hold it up to our hearts and our lives to see where we miss the mark. You will be led to go before the Lord and confess.

T - Thanksgiving

As we go to the Lord in Thanksgiving, we will express our gratitude to God for who He is and what He has done. We will thank Him for what we have learned about Him that day and for what He has revealed to us in His Word.

S - Supplication

When we approach God in Supplication, we will bring those study-related prayer requests before His throne. Instead of focusing on our circumstances, we will focus on what we have learned in His Word that day and ask Him to help us apply those truths to our lives.

SWORD STUDY VIEWS

1 -THE AERIAL VIEW

From our knees, we will move into our INVESTIGATIVE STUDY of the Bible. Your study begins with the AERIAL VIEW, in which you will read the entire book several times to help you become familiar with the text. This will show you the "lay of the land," like a photo taken from an airplane or a satellite. By researching the author, historical context and original recipients of the book, you will set the stage for more accurate understanding of the text. You will create your own book title that describes the central theme of the book. Your AERIAL VIEW observations will help you build a solid and true foundation for all that you will learn in the upcoming weeks. The AERIAL VIEW will be covered in Week One as we investigate the author, recipient, and the historical context of the book.

2 - THE STREETVIEW

As we continue, we will explore the book from a STREETVIEW perspective, going in for a closer look and focusing in on one chapter at a time. The STREETVIEW involves several exercises. First, you will make general observations of the chapter by looking for exhortations, commands, topics, or lists. Then, you will literally be interviewing the chapter by asking who, what, when, where, why, and how questions. This exercise will be like knocking on someone's door and asking them questions. Next, you will search the chapter for any key words. Finally, from these observations, you will choose a title for the chapter. In addition, as part of the daily INVESTIGATIVE STUDY, you will read through the chapter being studied, making any new or revised observations of the chapter.

3 - UNDER THE RUG

UNDER THE RUG is when we really dig deep to uncover any hidden details. In this step, we will be identifying specific key words and looking up the original Greek words and their meanings. We refer to this step as a "Word Study." We will also look up cross references for the Key Words. These are Scriptures in other parts of the Bible that will provide deeper understanding and context for the Key Word.

APPLY!

APPLY! is where we put it all together – from all the different views – to find what God reveals to us through our study of His Word. This will happen at different levels, depending on where you are in the chapter and on what part of the INVESTIGATIVE STUDY process you are in. Until you finish the UNDER THE RUG level, the *APPLY!* step will pertain in a general way to what you studied that day. Then on the last day of each chapter, you will have an opportunity to summarize through the unique "Day 10 Diagram". Finally, you will be able to apply what you have studied to how you live.

A.C.T.S. PRAYER MODEL

A.C.T.S. PRAYER MODEL

Prayer is key.

Prayer is the expression of our heart towards the Lord and is essential in our one-on-one relationship with Him. Building a regular time of prayer with the Lord is one of the most important things for us to do. We have been given direct access to God Most High. We want to make it a priority.

Prayer is an important work the Lord has given for us to do because He has called us to be His representatives, His agents here on earth. Our prayers can have a huge impact. James 5:16 says, *"The effective prayer of a righteous man can accomplish much"* (NASB). Before Jesus left His disciples, He told them something pretty incredible: *"Truly, truly, I say to you, he who believes in Me, the works that I do shall he do also; and greater works than these shall he do; because I go to the Father. And whatever you ask in My name, that will I do, that the Father may be glorified in the Son. If you ask Me anything in My name, I will do it."* (John 14:12-14 NASB)

Prayer is to be regular and intentional. We want to make the most of what we have been given. You can hear from Paul that we are to be constant and deliberate about prayer: *"With all prayer and petition pray at all times in the Spirit, and with this in view, be on the alert with all perseverance and petition for all the saints"* (Ephesians 6:18 NASB) and *"pray without ceasing."* (1 Thessalonians 5:17 NASB)

If prayer is this important, we want to learn how to pray. The disciples asked Jesus to teach them to pray, and Jesus gave them a model prayer that they could use. We see from this that it is helpful to have a model to go by. It will help us be more effective, efficient, and God-focused in our prayers. So, in the next few pages we will present an easy-to-remember prayer model to use whenever you approach your heavenly Father in prayer. It will help you build a God-centered relationship with the Lord, be deliberate and intentional in prayer, and be a mighty prayer warrior that accomplishes much for the kingdom of God.

A.C.T.S. PRAYER MODEL

A

ADORATION

Adoration is worshiping God for who He is and what He has done. It teaches us to focus specifically on His character, all of His attributes, and His wonderful deeds. It draws attention to His Name. God's Name represents the fullness of everything that God is and does. Take your eyes off of yourself and your circumstances. Fix your eyes upon God the Father, God the Son, and God the Holy Spirit. As you study the book of 1 John and read through various Scriptures, focus on God's character and praise him for it. Focus on who He is. He is your Father, your Almighty God, the LORD!

Let's practice praising God by using His Word, first in 1 Peter and then in Revelation:

> 1 Peter 1:3-4 (NASB) *Blessed be the God and Father of our Lord Jesus Christ, who according to His great mercy has caused us to be born again to a living hope through the resurrection of Jesus Christ from the dead, 4 to obtain an inheritance which is imperishable and undefiled and will not fade away, reserved in heaven for you,*

"O Lord God, You are the God and Father of our Lord and Saviour Jesus Christ. You are the giver of life. You have caused us to be born again to a living hope. You are our true inheritance."

> Revelation 4:8-11 (NASB) *And the four living creatures, each one of them having six wings, are full of eyes around and within; and day and night they do not cease to say, "HOLY, HOLY, HOLY, is THE LORD GOD, THE ALMIGHTY, WHO WAS AND WHO IS AND WHO IS TO COME." 9 And when the living creatures give glory and honour and thanks to Him who sits on the throne, to Him who lives forever and ever, 10 the twenty-four elders will fall down before Him who sits on the throne, and will worship Him who lives forever and ever, and will cast their crowns before the throne, saying,*
> *11 "Worthy art Thou, our Lord and our God, to receive glory and honour and power; for Thou didst create all things, and because of Thy will they existed, and were created."*

"Lord God Almighty, Maker of heaven and earth, You are in control. You sit in heaven and see all that man does. You are the King of kings. You appoint kings and put them in places. You have placed Jesus on Your holy mountain. There is nothing I need to fear for You are God and there is no other."

A.C.T.S. PRAYER MODEL

C

CONFESSION

Confessing your sin is as simple as saying, "God, I did the wrong thing." He wants us to be very specific and say exactly what we thought, said, or did that was not according to His Word. Knowing God's Word is the best way to know what is right and what is wrong. Anytime we know what is right and do not do it, it is sin. But even if we don't know what is right and we do wrong it is sin. So it is best to know God's Word. Lay your heart in your hands and lift it up to God. Confess your fear, your weakness, your grumbling – whatever your sin. During the day, when you sin, confess it immediately.

Let's practice confessing your sin by using God's Word, first in 1 Peter and then in the Psalms:

1 Peter 2:1-3 (NKJV) *Therefore, laying aside all malice, all deceit, hypocrisy, envy, and all evil speaking, 2 as newborn babes, desire the pure milk of the word, that you may grow thereby, 3 if indeed you have tasted that the Lord is gracious.*

"Heavenly Father, I confess that I am prone to wander and I say things that I shouldn't. Please forgive me and renew my heart so that I may desire the pure milk of the Word, that I may grow strong in You."

Psalm 51:1-4 (NKJV) *Have mercy upon me, O God, according to Your lovingkindness; according to the multitude of Your tender mercies, blot out my transgressions. 2 Wash me thoroughly from my iniquity, and cleanse me from my sin. 3 For I acknowledge my transgressions, and my sin is always before me. 4 Against You, You only, have I sinned, and done this evil in Your sight – that You may be found just when You speak, and blameless when You judge.*

David, the psalmist, knows God's loving-kindness and compassion. He openly seeks God's forgiveness for his sin. Do you need to ask God to forgive your hard heart and ask Him to give you a heart like David's? "Lord Jesus, I am so sorry. I do not meditate on your Word day and night. I do not love Your Word like David loves Your Word. Please change my heart." 1 John 1:9 reminds us, *"If we confess our sins, He is faithful and just to forgive us our sins and to cleanse us from all unrighteousness* (NKJV)."

A.C.T.S. PRAYER MODEL

T

THANKSGIVING

Thanksgiving is expressing gratitude to God for who He is and what He has done. Thanksgiving gets personal. It acknowledges that He does not just do mighty deeds – He does mighty deeds for me. It recognizes that God is not just a wonderful God – He is a wonderful God for me. What should we thank God for? Everything! "Rejoice always, pray without ceasing, give thanks in all circumstances; for this is the will of God in Christ Jesus for you" (1 Thessalonians 5:16-18 ESV). This means the hard stuff – even the stuff that is painful and that we might not feel particularly thankful for.

Let's practice thanking God by using His Word, first in 1 Peter and then in the Psalms:

> 1 Peter 1:8-9 (ESV) *Though you have not seen him, you love him. Though you do not now see him, you believe in him and rejoice with joy that is inexpressible and filled with glory, 9 obtaining the outcome of your faith, the salvation of your souls."*

"Heavenly Father, I rejoice and give great thanks to You. My heart is full of joy and gratefulness for my salvation and all You have done through your Son. Thank You, Jesus. I do love You and believe in You. You have redeemed me, and because of You I am forgiven for my sins. I praise You and I thank You. You are good and You are merciful to give me what I do not deserve."

> Psalm 107:1-3 (ESV) *Oh give thanks to the LORD, for he is good, for his steadfast love endures forever! Let the redeemed of the LORD say so, whom he has redeemed from trouble and gathered in from the lands, from the east and from the west, from the north and from the south.*

"Father God, I thank You so much for Your goodness and Your loving-kindness towards me. I thank You that Your loving-kindness is so constant and reliable – it is everlasting and will never fail. You have redeemed me from the clutches of Satan and have gathered me into Your kingdom. You have taken me from a far off land where I was distant from You and gathered me to Yourself. I praise You and thank You for how far You were willing to go to bring me near to You."

A.C.T.S. PRAYER MODEL

S

SUPPLICATION

Supplication is asking God on behalf of others or yourself. When we ask God for help, it nurtures a sense of dependence on Him for everything in our lives. And, since we have so many needs, this will probably be the easiest prayer step for many of us. "And pray in the Spirit on all occasions with all kinds of prayers and requests. With this in mind, be alert and always keep on praying for all the saints" (Ephesians 6:18, NIV). Make a special list of the people God has put in your life and note ways you can lift up their particular needs in prayer.

Supplication is bringing your requests before God on behalf of yourself and others. Let's practice speaking to Him using His Word in 1 Peter:

> 1 Peter 1:13-21 (NIV) *Therefore, prepare your minds for action; be self-controlled; set your hope fully on the grace to be given you when Jesus Christ is revealed. 14 As obedient children, do not conform to the evil desires you had when you lived in ignorance. 15 But just as he who called you is holy, so be holy in all you do; 16 for it is written: "Be holy, because I am holy." 17 Since you call on a Father who judges each man's work impartially, live your lives as strangers here in reverent fear. 18 For you know that it was not with perishable things such as silver or gold that you were redeemed from the empty way of life handed down to you from your forefathers, 19 but with the precious blood of Christ, a lamb without blemish or defect. 20 He was chosen before the creation of the world, but was revealed in these last times for your sake. 21 Through him you believe in God, who raised him from the dead and glorified him, and so your faith and hope are in God.*

"Heavenly Father, help me prepare my mind for action! Help me be self-controlled so that I may set my mind, heart, and energy towards following after You and You alone! I want to be holy as You are holy. Please show me the way. Please mold me and make me. Help me remember that You have bought me with the precious blood of Your Son and my Saviour, Jesus Christ. May I live only to serve You and bring glory to Your name and no other!"

FAMILY BONFIRE

Hear, O Israel: The LORD our God, the LORD is one. You shall love the LORD your God with all your heart and with all your soul and with all your might. And these words that I command you today shall be on your heart. You shall teach them diligently to your children, and shall talk of them when you sit in your house, and when you walk by the way, and when you lie down, and when you rise. You shall bind them as a sign on your hand, and they shall be as frontlets between your eyes. You shall write them on the doorposts of your house and on your gates.

~ *Deuteronomy 6:4-9 (ESV)* ~

Dear Diligent Parent,

As parents, God has given us the responsibility and privilege of discipling our children to walk with Him through Jesus Christ. Our goal is to come alongside you in that exciting endeavour by providing resources, ideas and encouragement as you shepherd your children, under our perfect Great Shepherd. This is where the Sword Studies and Family Bonfire fit in.

The Sword Study teaches a step by step, in-depth pattern of Bible study for you and your children together. The "Sword Study Overview" will give you and idea of what each week and day will look like.

We highly encourage you to study alongside your children by using the Senior Sword Study, both for your own benefit and personal growth, as well as for an enhanced ability to lead them in their learning and spiritual growth.

It is a time commitment, which will take away from other pursuits. We live busy lives and have an enemy who works hard to distract us in many ways, so it will take a determined effort to keep Christ in the center of our day-to-day lives.

While you could just do the studies as independent family members, we feel that the opportunity to really disciple your children lies in making the time to have a "Family Bonfire" each week.

This is a planned time of family fellowship, intentional discipleship and sharing all that the Lord has taught each of you through the week. It provides mutual encouragement to stay the course, and helps parents to see where and how their children are growing, struggling, learning and asking questions. Of course, some of these benefits can be accomplished spontaneously through day-to-day discussions, but having a planned time makes sure that the busyness of life doesn't swamp the conversation and mutual edification that is so essential to intentional discipleship. Having a set-aside time for fun and spiritual growth as a family also demonstrates to your children what is really important in life.

The rest of this section provides tools to support you in this commitment. We have provided suggestions and a framework on how to accomplish having Family Bonfires each week throughout the summer. They are suggestions and not formulas. You can customize and adapt what we have laid out so that it best suits your family's needs.

We suggest that you hold your Family Bonfire time each weekend, after completing the scheduled five days of the Sword Study.

We have included fun ideas for food and activities to make the Family Bonfires something that everyone anticipates. Additionally, we have provided weekly summaries as snapshots of the content covered in the Sword Studies each week. If some weeks' schedules don't allow you to do the full study yourself, you can still keep up with the kids via these summaries.

The first Family Bonfire of the season will serve as a Kick-Off for the whole study. The following weeks will follow a pattern of opening with prayer, Scripture reading and worship and then family discussion questions. Everyone should bring their Bibles and Sword Studies.

The family discussion questions will include review questions that cover factual knowledge gained from the study and life application questions that draw out the deeper impact of delving into God's Word. On the weeks that contain Day 10 Diagrams, you will review that material. As a parent, be sure to share what God taught you as well.

Always remember to seek God's heart and will during these times. When our hearts and minds are submissive to the Spirit of God, He can do great things. The relationships you are building with each other, with the Lord, and with His Word will be life-long and eternal. The benefit to your family may be far beyond anything you can ask or imagine (Ephesians 3:20).

F A M I L Y   B O N F I R E

S Y L L A B U S

KICK-OFF BONFIRE
Weekend before family begins Sword Study

WEEK 1:   **OVERVIEW**

WEEK 2:   **1 JOHN CHAPTER 1,** *STREETVIEW*

WEEK 3:   **1 JOHN CHAPTER 1,** *UNDER THE RUG*
                 Day 10 Diagram

WEEK 4:   **1 JOHN CHAPTER 2,** *STREETVIEW*

WEEK 5:   **1 JOHN CHAPTER 2,** *UNDER THE RUG*
                 Day 10 Diagram

WEEK 6:   **1 JOHN CHAPTER 3,** *STREETVIEW*

WEEK 7:   **1 JOHN CHAPTER 3,** *UNDER THE RUG*
                 Day 10 Diagram

WEEK 8:   **1 JOHN CHAPTER 4,** *STREETVIEW*

WEEK 9:   **1 JOHN CHAPTER 4,** *UNDER THE RUG*
                 Day 10 Diagram

WEEK 10:   **1 JOHN CHAPTER 5,** *STREETVIEW*

WEEK 11:   **1 JOHN CHAPTER 5,** *UNDER THE RUG*
                 Day 10 Diagram

WEEK 12:   **REVIEW**

KICK-OFF BONFIRE

"GET READY!"

Prepare: Read through your Parent Guidebook Sword Study Overview, A.C.T.S. Prayer Model and Family Bonfire Sections. Bring a calendar and your Parent Guidebook. Have all of your family members bring their Sword Studies, Bibles and Bible Memory Cards. The purpose of the Kick-Off Bonfire is to get your family prepared and excited for a summer in God's Word through the Sword Studies.

One practical step to accomplish before or during your first Bonfire is to organize your family's Bible Memory Cards. You may want to mark each child's cards with their initials, or with a certain color of marker or sticker. Some find it helpful to hole-punch a corner of the cards and store them on a ring for ease of use.

We have provided a suggested syllabus for your planning purposes. Either ahead of time, or together at the Family Bonfire, plan the dates for all of your Bonfires. Do you have a vacation planned? Can you have a special Bonfire there, or make adjustments on the week that you come back home? Does Dad have a business trip? Perhaps you could still hold a Bonfire with the use of Skype. The point is to have a plan ahead of time, so that your time together for the Family Bonfire is not buried under the normal busyness of life.

Creative Family Ideas for Kick-Off Bonfire – Theme, "On Your Mark, Get Set, Go!"
• Each week in this part of your Family Bonfire area, we will give you several ideas to add fun to your weekend that also ties into the theme of the week's Sword Study lessons and Bible Memory recommendation.
• For your weekly "Bonfire," find a comfortable spot for your whole family to gather. You may want to have a special meal, snacks or even a campfire, if you have the facilities. Cultivate the atmosphere for a fun family gathering, a "family party night" that everyone looks forward to all week.
• After this "Get Ready!" section, each week the next page will give a suggested outline for a Family Bonfire that corresponds with the material and study of the specific week's lessons. Again, this is not meant to be a formula, only a launching pad for what works for your family.
• Hide a small treasure for each child or one family item. Allow everyone to go find their treasure using simple clues. Gather back at your Bonfire and talk about how God's Word is a hidden treasure to us. Discuss the importance of spending time studying the Bible as you kick-off your Sword Study.
• Plan a special dinner at a local Turkish restaurant to highlight the start of your family time in 1 John. Discuss how John would have been in Ephesus and note the atmosphere of the restaurant.
• Find or print off a map of modern day Turkey. Bring it to your Bonfire with a globe to help your family have a good understanding of where John was located as he wrote 1 John.

KICK-OFF BONFIRE SCHEDULE

Begin with Prayer

Worship:

Sing hymns and/or songs focused on the Lord's attributes.
Have your children look through their Bible Memory Cards and share a passage that they already know.

Read Scripture:

Psalm 111 *(Divide the chapter and have each family member read a few verses.)*

Family Discussion Questions:

What is the theme of Psalm 111?
(Praising the Lord; verse 1 and 10)

How are we to praise the Lord?
(We are to praise the Lord with all of our hearts, according to verse 1.)

What is done with all the works of the Lord?
(According to verse 2, the works of the Lord are sought out, studied and pondered by those who have pleasure and delight in them.)

Have each of you organized a special place to do your Bible Study?

Do you have any concerns about starting your Sword Study that we can all pray for this week?

Bible Memory Recommendation (for upcoming week):

Psalm 111:10, Jeremiah 9:23-24

Close:

Read Psalm 111:10 and Jeremiah 9:23-24 to your family. May these passages be an encouagement to your family as you choose to seek understanding and knowledge of God through His Word as a family!

Close in prayer as a family by going around the circle, first in Adoration, then Confession, then Thanksgiving, and concluding with Supplication.

WEEK ONE

"GET READY!"

Prepare: Complete the Senior Sword Study Week 1 **OR** read 1 John.

Quick Notes: The Sword Study students completed Week 1 by observing the book of 1 John from an AERIAL VIEW. Each day they began with prayer and a time of writing cross reference Scriptures that encouraged them to gain wisdom through the study of God's Word. During the inductive study portion, they studied the author by looking at various Scriptures throughout the Bible and investigated the false teaching of John's day, Gnosticism, for an understanding of the historical context of 1 John. To close the week, on Day 5 the students were asked to title, summarize and choose a key verse for each chapter from their initial observations of 1 John. After the study section each day, they were encouraged to pray using the A.C.T.S. prayer model.

Summary: 1 John was a letter written by John, a close friend of Jesus, to the Christians who were being troubled by the false teachings of the Gnostic teachers. John had left his occupation as a fisherman to become a disciple of Christ. Although he was known as a "Son of Thunder" for his dynamic personality, this letter has a gentle, fatherly tone throughout the chapters. John repetitively shares his reasons for writing this letter to the body of Christ. His style is one of circling by repetition and zeroing in on his main purposes of assuring and encouraging his readers of their salvation through Jesus and fellowship with the Father, Son and other believers. John's words thunder through history to us as current day students of the Word: "God is light! God is love! Beloved children of God, love Him with all your hearts, minds and souls! Walk in His light!"

Creative Family Ideas for the weekend – Theme: "Getting to know John"
• Take your family fishing. Pack your lunch and enjoy the day at the lake or pond. For the super-adventurous, bring materials for a campfire and plan to eat your catch. Make sure to have some "Plan B" items in case the fish aren't biting! There are lots of good talking points around fishing…
• Purchase a children's game of "Let's Go Fishing." Or, have a craft day making a set of your own pretend fishing set with dowel rods, string, paper, markers and lamination pages from your local craft or super store. Play the game at your Family Bonfire; regardless of the ages of your children, everyone can have fun playing. To make it even more exciting, use a children's pool as the pond.
• Play "Follow the Leader" or "Mother May I?" and then explain how being a disciple is following Jesus, and how He lived and cared for others.
• Watch a historical speech and discuss how the speaker is dynamic and resembles "thunder." Make the correlation between the speaker and how John was named by Jesus in Mark 3:16-18. Speech possibilities could include: Martin Luther's "I Have a Dream," John F. Kennedy's 1961 Inaugural Address ("Ask not what your country can do…"), or an apologetic presentation by Ray Comfort, Billy Graham, John Stonestreet, Del Tackett or Ravi Zacharias.

WEEK ONE

Begin with Prayer

Read Scripture:
Read Matthew 4:17-25 and Psalm 29

Worship:
Sing "I Will Follow" by Chris Tomlin, hymns (such as "As The Deer") and/or other worship songs.
Share memorized verses

Family Discussion Questions:
Who was the author of 1 John?
(John, the son of Zebedee)

What did you learn about the author?
(Fisherman, Son of Zebedee, Brother to James, Matthew 4:17-24; Disciple of Jesus Christ, Matthew 10:1-2; Present with Jesus during transfiguration, Mark 9:1-2; Part of Jesus' inner circle, close friend, Mark 14:31-41; Prisoner on Patmos and Bondservant of God, Revelation 1:1, 9-11)

What philosophy were the false prophets teaching during the time of John's letter?
(Gnosticism)

Describe Gnosticism.
(Answers will vary in depth. General definition of Gnosticism is "a teaching that depended on knowledge as the end-all of salvation." Gnostic teachers believed God was only a spirit, and that Jesus either did not come to earth or was not God.)

Have each family member share their chapter titles for the five chapters of 1 John.
(Answers will vary)

Ask if anyone has a personal prayer need that the rest of the family can pray for this week.

Bible Memory Recommendation (for upcoming week):
John 8:12, John 17:3

Close:
Read John 8:12 and John 17:3.
Close in prayer as a family by going around the circle, first in Adoration, then Confession, then Thanksgiving, and concluding with Supplication.

W E E K   T W O

"GET READY!"

Prepare: Complete the Senior Sword Study Week 2 **OR** read 1 John.

Write: Your children have started writing the book of 1 John. They have written out the text of 1 John 1:1-6. Using the "My Copy of 1 John" section in your Sword Study Parent Guidebook, catch up to them by writing these six verses of 1 John 1.

Quick Notes: The Sword Study students lowered their perspective's view from the big picture to a more detailed look at 1 John 1 this week. All levels began by interviewing the chapter. While the younger learners took two days to accomplish the interview exercise, the Junior and Senior Sword Study students gathered lists, exhortations and comparisons from 1 John 1. During Days 3 and 4, they looked at specific phrases in 1 John in light of other passages scattered throughout Scripture to gain a better background understanding. Everyone closed the week learning about the word study process in preparation for next week's UNDER THE RUG level.

Summary: John jumped right into his letter to the church without a self-introduction or greetings. He immediately declares his witness of Jesus' presence on the earth, in the flesh. Declaring that he had seen, heard and witnessed Jesus himself, John makes his case as a knowledgeable preacher of the truth to us, as well as to those confused by Gnosticism's claims. Next, he shares that the message he and the other disciples heard from Jesus was that God is light and there is no darkness in Him. True believers walk in the light, fellowship with one another and have salvation through Jesus' blood. We chose 1 John 1:3 as the key verse.

Creative Family Ideas for the weekend – Theme: "Light"
• Play a game of flashlight tag with your family.
• Investigate nocturnal animals. How do they see so well in the dark?
• Play "Hide & Seek" with glow-in-the-dark bracelets- hide around a room or your whole
    house!
• Have your Family Bonfire by candlelight or flashlight.
• Using glow-in-the-dark paint, create poster board signs. Place them all around a room with passages. Or create a treasure hunt using the signs. Leave them turned around until after your Family Bonfire, then turn off the lights and begin your hunt.
• Discuss how everyone feels when they are in the dark. What happens when you walk around in the dark? Pair off in two's and take turns walking around blind-folded without assistance. (The partners without the blind folds make sure that no one gets hurt!)

W E E K   T W O

Begin with Prayer

Read Scripture:
Read Psalm 27 and 1 Peter 2:9-12

Worship:
Sing "10,000 Reasons" by Matt Redman, or sing other hymns or worship songs
Share memorized verses

Family Discussion Questions:
What name did John call Jesus in the beginning of his letter?
(Word of Life; 1 John 1:1)

Name the ways John claimed to have witnessed Jesus on earth, in the flesh.
(John saw, heard, touched and walked with Jesus while he was a man on earth, 1 John 1:1)

**John made two comparisons in 1 John 1; he compared light with _____
and truth with _____?**
(Light to darkness, 1 John 1:5 and truth to lie, 1 John 1:6)

Turn to your Week 2 Day 3 investigative study and share something that you learned about one of John's phrases.
(Answers will vary.)

Ask if anyone has a personal prayer need that the rest of the family can pray for this week.

Bible Memory Recommendation (for upcoming week):
1 John 1:3, 1 John 1:9

Close:
Read 1 John 1:3 and 9.
Close in prayer as a family by going around the circle, first in Adoration, then Confession, then Thanksgiving, and concluding with Supplication.

WEEK THREE

"GET READY!"

Prepare: Complete the Senior Sword Study Week 3 **OR** read 1 John.

Write: Write verses 7 through 10 of 1 John 1 in your "Write!" section of the Parent Guidebook. Using the symbols below, mark any references to God that you find in Chapter 1.

God the Father   God the Son   God the Holy Spirit

Quick Notes: Students finished their spotlight on 1 John 1 this week. They did this through the UNDER THE RUG activities of word studies and cross referencing. We chose *fellowship* and *sin* as the two Key Words for Chapter 1. They learned the Greek words, their transliterations and definitions. Next, they investigated passages outside of 1 John that used *fellowship* and *sin*. Everyone was introduced to their first Day 10 Diagram on Day 5, which is a pictorial summary of 1 John 1.

Summary: God is Light and He does not fellowship in the darkness. It is only through His Son, Jesus, that He can have a relationship with us and see us without sin. As a result of the event we call "salvation," He looks at us, sees us wrapped in Jesus' righteousness, and accepts us as His adopted children; otherwise, He sees us wrapped in our sin and, as a perfect God, cannot enter into a relationship with us. If we have trusted Jesus as our payment for sin, we have the seed of Christ, the Holy Spirit, dwelling in us. Then, we have not only been saved from the penalty of sin, which is death, but have victorious power over sin's bondage and are able to walk in the Light.

Creative Family Ideas for the weekend – Theme: "Fellowship"

• Plan a progressive fellowship dinner with like-minded friends next week. Create the invitations, brainstorm and plan as a family at this week's Bonfire. Be sure to plan for time to talk about all the Lord is doing!

• Gather the materials to create friendship bracelets.

• Either do or show one another your Day 10 Diagrams of 1 John 1.

• Join with another family for your Bonfire time.

WEEK THREE

Begin with Prayer

Read Scripture:
Read Acts 2:42-47 and Philippians 2:1-7

Worship:
Sing or listen to "Power of the Cross" by the Gettys, sing hymns or other songs
Share memorized verses

Family Discussion Questions:
Since one of your word studies was about fellowship, describe what you learned about fellowship this week.
(Various answers. General, paraphrased definition of Christian fellowship is "gathering of like-minded Believers to pray, hear preaching or worship God.")

What is sin?
(An action against God's rules)

Who has sinned?
(Everyone has sinned, Romans 3:23)

Before we can fellowship with God, we must have a relationship. How do we get a relationship with God?
(We must confess with our mouth that Jesus is Lord and believe He was raised from the dead, Romans 10:9-10)

What does sin do to our fellowship with God?
(Sin breaks our fellowship with God. He wants us to confess our sin to restore fellowship, 1 John 1:9)

Review the "Day 10 Diagram" and ask if there are any questions. Ask each family member to share his or her diagram.
(A completed Diagram is on the next page for your reference. Often, children are excited to share their colored creations!)

Ask if anyone has a personal prayer need that the rest of the family can pray for this week.

Bible Memory Recommendation (for upcoming week):
Job 15:14-16, Proverbs 28:13-14

Close: Read Psalm 130. Close in prayer as a family by going around the circle first in Adoration, then Confession, then Thanksgiving, and concluding with Supplication.

Title: **Walk in the Light!**
Key Verse: 1 John 1:3

Chapter: **One**
♥ :Psalms 111:10, Jeremiah 9:23-24
John 8:12, John 17:3
1 John 1:3, 1 John 1:9

Greek Words: Fellowship & Sin

~~ Koinonia:
Partnership, Fellow Traveler

~~ Hamartano/Hamartia:
To Trespass/An Offense

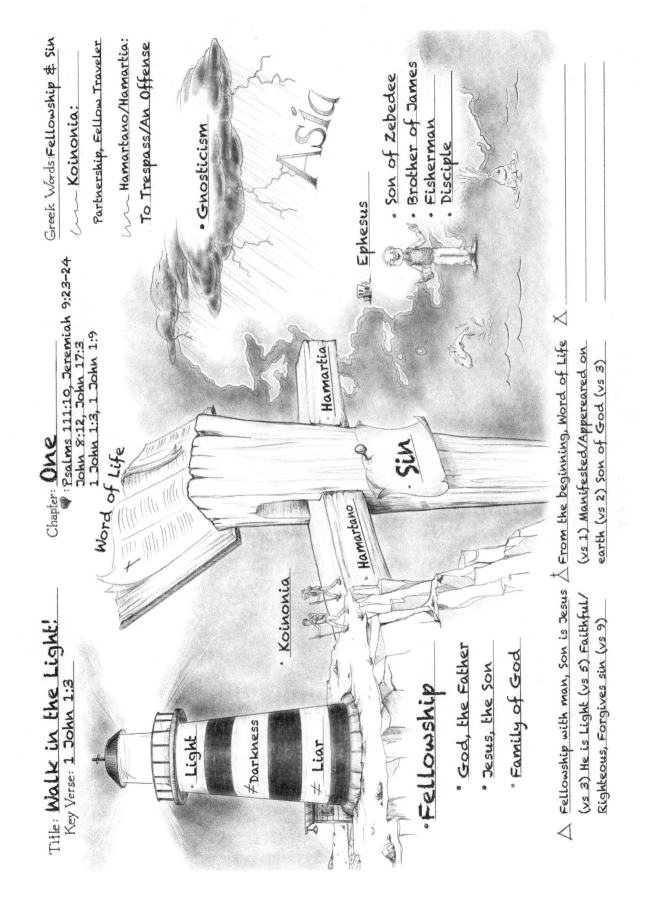

Word of Life

Hamartia

Sin

Hamartano

· Koinonia

·Gnosticism

Asia

Ephesus

· Son of Zebedee
· Brother of James
· Fisherman
· Disciple

·Light
≠Darkness
≠ Liar

·Fellowship
· God, the Father
· Jesus, the Son
· Family of God

△ Fellowship with man, Son is Jesus △ From the beginning, Word of Life △
(vs 3) He is Light (vs 5) Faithful/ (vs 1) Manifested/Appeared on
Righteous, Forgives sin (vs 9) earth (vs 2) Son of God (vs 3)

35

WEEK FOUR

"GET READY!"

Prepare: Complete the Senior Sword Study Week 4 **OR** read 1 John and Chapter 2 twice.

Write: To keep in step with your children's investigation of 1 John 2, write verses 1-16 in your Parent Guidebook.

Quick Notes: During the first two days of Week 4 your explorers focused on 1 John 2 by writing short, summary phrases of the 29 verses of this chapter. John repeated the phrases, "I write" and "I have written." On Day 3, everyone noted his reasons for writing. The Senior and Junior Sword Studies highlighted the many "If-Then" statements on Day 4. Everyone wrapped up their STREETVIEW of 1 John 2 by looking at John's exhortations, unfamiliar words and choosing Key Words.

Summary: John addresses his readers: fathers, young men, children. Each of the titles John uses portrays a fatherly term of endearment. There is no doubt that the once "Son of Thunder" has softened a bit and is displaying fatherly love to his children in the faith. In this chapter, John gives "his children" assurance of their status in Christ and resulting eternal life. An exhortation not to love the things of the world is particularly poignant to his audience both in the past and present. We chose 1 John 2:13 as the key verse.

Creative Family Ideas for the weekend – Theme: "The World"
• Use this week's lesson as an opportunity to weed through your family's belongings for things that are unused and donate them to a good cause.
• Play a family game of Monopoly. Talk about how easy it is to get excited about money and property!
• Take a week's fast from sports, television, or technology.
• Calculate the cost of your family attending an event, and dontate the cost to a ministry.

W E E K F O U R

Begin with Prayer

Read Scripture:
Read Isaiah 46:5-13 and Psalm 90

Worship:
Sing hymns and/or worship songs
Share memorized verses

Family Discussion Questions:
What is an "advocate?"
(A person who pleads the case of another.)

Who is our Advocate?
(Jesus is our Advocate.,1 John 2:1)

What is "propitiation?"
(Payment for a debt)

Why do we need propitiation from God?
(To pay the debt for our sin, 1 John 2:2)

What are some of the titles that John used for his recipients in 1 John 2?
(Little children, verse 1; Fathers, verse 13; Young men, verse 13; Children, verse 18)

What three exhortations/commands did John give in Chapter 2?
(Day 5: Do not love the world, nor things in it, verse 15; Abide in what you heard in the beginning, verse 24; Abide in Jesus, verse 28.)

Ask if anyone has a personal prayer need that the rest of the family can pray for this week.

Bible Memory Recommendation (for the upcoming week):
Psalm 36:7-10, John 8:31-32

Close:
Read Psalm 36:7-10 and John 8:31-32.
Close in prayer as a family by going around the circle, first in Adoration, then Confession, then Thanksgiving, and concluding with Supplication.

WEEK FIVE

"GET READY!"

Prepare: Complete the Senior Sword Study Week 5 **OR** read 1 John.

Write: Your children have finished writing 1 John, Chapter 2; you can do the same in your "Write!" pages. Mark any references to God.

Quick Notes: "I *know* the President because I <u>saw</u> his picture in the newspaper."
"I *know* the President because I was his <u>personal</u> assistant for 10 years."

In the small letter of 1 John, there are 30 occurrences of two different Greek words both of which are translated "know" in English. Students learned the first Greek word, *eido*, means a surface knowledge of someone or something, similar to "see" or "perceive." The second, *ginosko*, means to have a growing, deepening personal knowledge of someone. How amazing to watch John effectively use these two words to show us the differences between true Christianity and the false teaching of the Gnostics! They also studied the Greek word for *abide*, meaning "to remain, dwell or live with another in heart, mind and will" or "to remain steadfast." After studying each word, each level took deeper looks by cross referencing various passages with the words *know* and *abide*.

Summary: John emphasized the importance of the different levels of knowledge. There would be many that said they knew God, but only those who *abided* by His ways were truly of Him. John gave pointers on how to evaluate one's true identity. Did they love their brother? Were they walking in the light? Have they remained with us? Carefully, in fatherly love, he assured them that they *know* Jesus and the word of God *abides* in them. We chose verse 13 as the key verse.

Creative Family Ideas for the weekend – Theme: "Abide"

• Play games that make family members stick together (abide), such as three-legged races or wheelbarrow races.
• Find the retro game of "Password" or create your own game of synonyms to play during your Bonfire.
• Build a fort and abide in it all day long with your younger crew. Plan to have the whole family attend dinner with you at the end of the day.
• Create popsicle stick houses and discuss how we are to dwell in Jesus' ways.
• Practice your week's Bible Memory passages by putting each word on a different piece of paper- mix them up and have family members race to put them in order.
• Enlarge your "Day 10 Diagram" to poster size or bigger for a group coloring activity at your Family Bonfire. (You have our permission to make one enlarged copy for your family!)
• Consider purchasing "The Hiding Place" in preparation for Week 8 or 9's Bonfire.

W E E K F I V E

Begin with Prayer

Read Scripture:
Read John 15:1-15

Worship:
Sing "He is the Vine & we are the branches….His banner over me is love!," hymns and/or songs
Share memorized verses

Family Discussion Questions:
Who is the vine? Who are the branches?
(Jesus is the vine, John 15:1) (Christians are the branches, John 15:2)

What does the word *abide* mean?
(To dwell, live, remain with another in mind, heart and will)

What happens when we *abide* with the vine?
(We have fruit that shows we are abiding in Jesus. We look like Him! John 15:2)

Who *abides* in our hearts?
(The Spirit of God, our Helper, Galatians 4:6)

What are the two meanings for *know* as John uses it in his letter?
(A casual knowledge like an acquaintance and a deep, intimate knowledge like a best friend.)

Review the "Day 10 Diagram". Ask each family member to share his or her diagram. (A completed Diagram is on the next page for your reference.)

Ask if anyone has a personal prayer need that the rest of the family can pray for this week.

Bible Memory Recommendation (for upcoming week):
2 Corinthians 6:16-18, Isaiah 43:1-2

Close:
Read 2 Corinthians 6:16-18 and Isaiah 43:1-2.
Close in prayer as a family by going around the circle, first in Adoration, then Confession, then Thanksgiving, and concluding with Supplication.

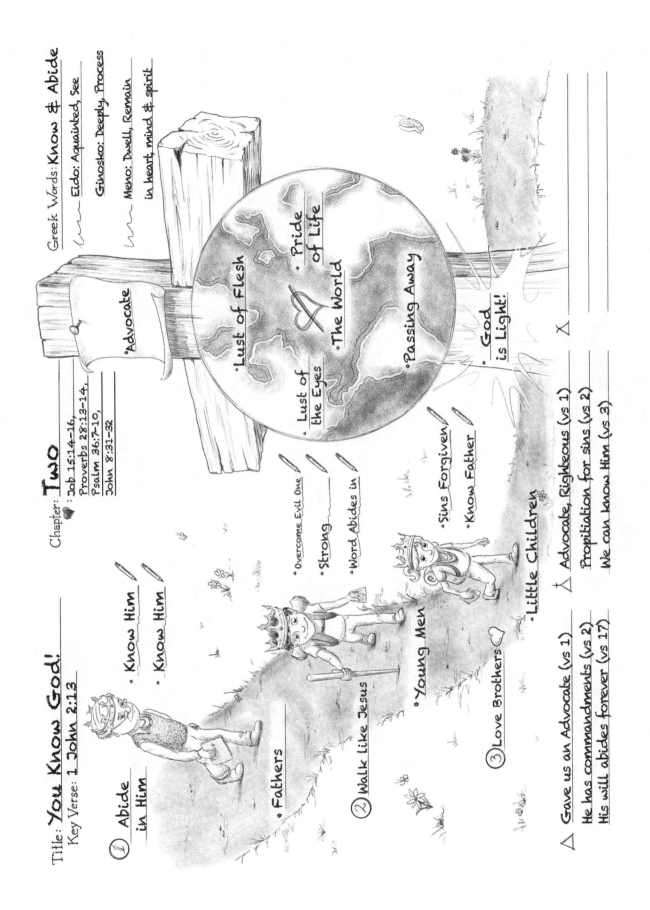

Title: **You Know God!**
Key Verse: 1 John 2:13

Greek Words: Know & Abide

⟶ Eido: Aquainted, See

⟶ Ginosko: Deeply, Process

⟶ Meno: Dwell, Remain
in heart, mind & spirit

Chapter: **Two**

🔲: Job 15:14-16,
Proverbs 28:13-14,
Psalm 36:7-10,
John 8:31-32

① Abide
    in Him

• Know Him /
• Know Him /

"Advocate"

• Lust of Flesh
• Pride of Life
• The World
• Lust of the Eyes
• Passing Away

• God is Light!

• Fathers

• Overcome Evil One /
• Strong
• Word Abides in /

② Walk like Jesus

• Young Men

• Sins Forgiven /
• Know Father /

③ Love Brothers 💙

• Little Children

△ Gave us an Advocate (vs 1)
He has commandments (vs 2)
His will abides forever (vs 17)

△ Advocate, Righteous (vs 1)
Propitiation for sins (vs 2)
We can know Him (vs 3)

X

41

W E E K   S I X

"GET READY!"

Prepare: Complete the Senior Sword Study Week 6 **OR** read 1 John and read Chapter 3 a second time.

Write: Begin writing 1 John 3 by copying verses 1 through 12.

Quick Notes: 1 John, Chapter 3 became the new focus this past week. The first days' assignment turned the tables on the students and made them ask questions of the chapter's verses. They spent the remainder of the week comparing the difference between the children of God and the children of the devil. John used Cain as an example of darkness, so on Day 5, everyone turned to Genesis to understand his story.

Summary: Chapter 3 begins with John describing the love of God as being so great that He gives us the right to be called children of God. He dwells on the attributes of God's children and then contrasts them to the behaviors of those who belong to the enemy of God, the devil. John once again takes the opportunity to present the gospel by highlighting our adoption into God's family through Jesus. We are not second-rate citizens, but full, birthright children of the Kingdom of Heaven.

Creative Family Ideas for the weekend – Theme: "Children of the King"
• Visit Steven Curtis Chapman's website, www.showhope.com, to learn more about adoption.
• Make crowns for whole family to wear at Family Bonfire.
• Create and act out a play about Esther.
• Watch the Veggie Tales *Queen Esther* movie.
• Ask your children who they have been praying for from Week 6, Day 4's Apply.
• Read a book or watch a DVD about Billy Graham.

W E E K   S I X

Begin with Prayer

Read Scripture:
Read Psalm 145:1-10 and Psalm 150:4-6

Worship:
  Sing hymns and/or worship songs
  Share memorized verses

Family Discussion Questions:
  Because God loves us so much, what does He call us?
  (His children, 1 John 3:1)

  What are the two groups of children?
  (Children of God and children of the devil, 1 John 3:10)

  What are the children of God supposed to practice?
  (The children of God practice righteousness, 1 John 3:10)

  How are the children of God supposed to love?
  (They are to love in word and deed, 1 John 3:18)

  Who is the Old Testament example used in 1 John Chapter 3?
  (Cain, the evil one, 1 John 3:12; Various answers, see Genesis 4:1-16)

  Ask if anyone has a personal prayer need that the rest of the family can pray for this week.

Bible Memory Recommendation (for upcoming week):
  2 Corinthians 5:20-21, Isaiah 45:22-23

Close:
Read 2 Corinthians 5:20-21 and Isaiah 45:22-23.
Close in prayer as a family by going around the circle, first in Adoration, then Confession, then Thanksgiving, and concluding with Supplication.

W E E K   S E V E N

"G E T   R E A D Y !"

Prepare: Complete the Senior Sword Study Week 7 **OR** read 1 John.

Write: Week 7 finished the in-depth look of 1 John 3; write the remaining verses in your Parent Guidebook. Mark any references to God in the chapter.

Quick Notes: Word studies of *righteous* and *righteousness* were the tasks of Week 7 for all levels. The children learned the details surrounding those that live in righteousness and were deemed righteous. Heroes of the faith, according to the Word of God, are those who walk in righteousness…in God's ways. The greatest example, of course, was Jesus. The youth investigated the lifestyles of the righteous examples and spent a day looking specifically at Jesus' life.

Summary: John emphasized the life of the children of God as being characterized by righteous living. They look different than those serving themselves and the enemy. God's children follow His commands, love one another and do not practice sin. The old adage of "practicing what you preach" comes from the 1 John 3:18 passage exhorting the children of God to love in word and deed. We will watch John zero in on this passage's message when we move into Chapter 4. We chose 1 John 3:1 as the key verse.

Creative Family Ideas for the weekend – Theme, "The righteous, holy and faithful… Heroes of the Faith"

• Bring your family to a fun, putt-putt golf course. At the conclusion of your game, announce the winner and then ask everyone if they realize the difference between these holes and the definition of holy. Use the opportunity to talk about the righteousness of God.

• Read a biography or watch a biographical DVD or a Heroes of the Faith DVD.

• Assign each member of the family a Hebrews 11 "Hero of the Faith" and have them act out a short skit.

• Play a game of charades using all heroes of the faith.

W E E K   S E V E N

Begin with Prayer

Read Scripture:
Read Hebrews 11:1-40 and Matthew 5:14-16.

Worship:
Sing hymns and/or worship songs
Share memorized verses

Family Discussion Questions:
<u>Review time!</u>
What type of writing is 1 John? *(Letter)*
What name did John call Jesus in the beginning of his letter? *(Word of Life, 1 John 1:1)*
What were the false teachers teaching? *(Gnosticism)*
Who has sinned? *(Everyone has sinned, Romans 3:23)*
Who is our Advocate? *(Jesus is our Advocate, 1 John 2:1)*
What is propitiation? *(Payment for a debt)*
What does the word *abide* mean? *(To dwell, live, remain with another in mind, heart and will)*

What is the definition of *righteous*?
(Doing what is right according to God's rules. God is the only One who is righteous without failure.)

The righteous children are busy, right? Name a few examples of righteous men you learned about.
(Answers will vary: Noah, Abraham, Cornelius, Simeon and Jesus are among those that were investigated.)

Review the "Day 10 Diagram" and ask if there are any questions. Ask each family member to share his or her diagram.
(A completed Diagram is on the next page for your reference.)

Ask if anyone has a personal prayer need that the rest of the family can pray for this week.

Bible Memory Recommendation (for upcoming week):
1 John 4:7-10, Philippians 3:8-11

Close: Read 1 John 4:7-10 and Philippians 3:8-11. Close in prayer as a family by going around the circle first, in Adoration, then Confession, then Thanksgiving, and concluding with Supplication.

Title: **God Loves Us!**
Key Verse: 1 John 3:1

Chapter: **Three**
: 2 Cor 6:16-18, 6:20-21
Isaih 43:1-2, 45:22-23

Greek Words: Righteous/ness
— Dikaios:
  holy, just

— Dikaiosune:
  Conforming to God's Law

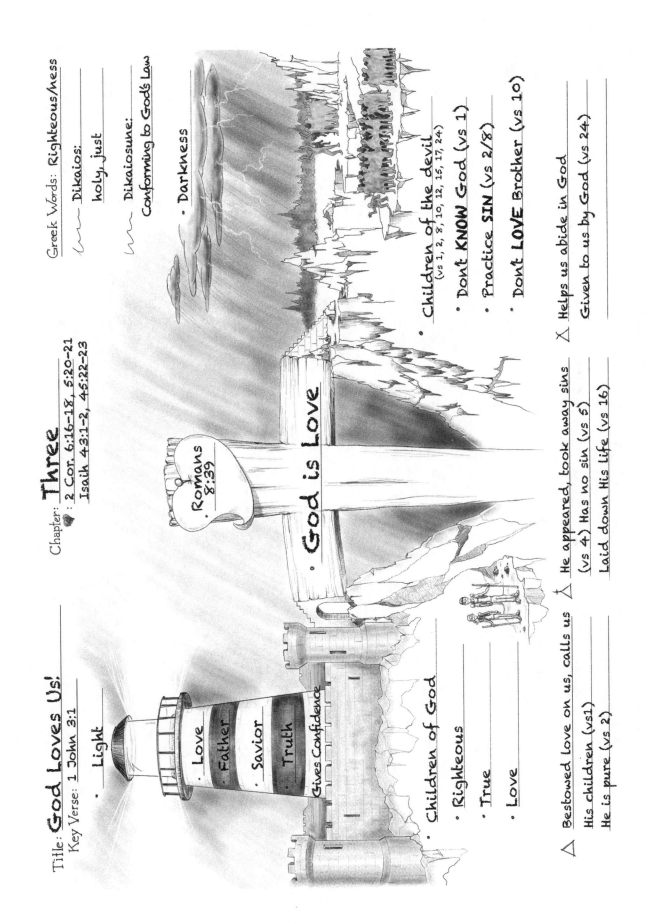

Romans 8:39

God is Love

- Light
  - Love
  - Father
  - Savior
  - Truth
  - Gives Confidence

- Children of God
  - Righteous
  - True
  - Love

△ Bestowed love on us, calls us
His children (vs1)
He is pure (vs 2)

✝ He appeared, took away sins
(vs 4) Has no sin (vs 5)
Laid down His life (vs 16)

- Darkness

- Children of the devil
  (vs 1, 2, 8, 10, 12, 15, 17, 24)
  · Don't KNOW God (vs 1)
  · Practice SIN (vs 2/8)
  · Don't LOVE Brother (vs 10)

✗ Helps us abide in God
Given to us by God (vs 24)

47

W E E K   E I G H T

"GET READY!"

Prepare: Complete Senior Sword Study Week 8 **OR** read 1 John and read Chapter 4 twice.

Write: Your children have been writing 1 John 4. They have reached verse 9 in their "Write!" pages. You will need to do the same to keep up with them!

Quick Notes: Students moved to 1 John 4 this week. They spent four days questioning and cross referencing phrases from Chapter 4. They summarized the gospel in their own words, with their own story, by using 1 John 4:4, 9 and 10 as they closed the week in Day 5. This week prepared students for next week's in-depth look at God's type of love by setting the stage of John's call to love the Lord our God with all our hearts, minds and wills above all. As a result, we are to love one another as well.

Summary: John describes the evidence of a child of God as his or her example of following God's commandments. The first commandment was to love the Lord with all their beings. The second was to love one another. These actions would show their association with Jesus. This fourth chapter of 1 John is all about love; the love God has for us, the love we have for Him and the love we are to have towards others. This is no ordinary love.

Creative Family Ideas for the weekend – Theme: "Commands"

• Bring back the basics of commands this week in your Family Bonfire! Play a game of "Mother May I?" or "Simon Says" or "Red light, Green light."
• Watch the classic movie, "The Ten Commandments," with popcorn and treats.
• Check out Geo-Caching. This is a free app that has millions of treasure hunts around the country. There is even one for the Sword Study, called "Sword Study Treasure." Talk about how following directions is the key to any successful hunt.
• Print out directions to a favorite park. Don't disclose your destination, and have one of your children be the co-pilot. Your co-pilot reads the map directions out loud to get you to the park. Have a picnic lunch there to celebrate.
• Set up a fun obstacle course. Make it complex. Begin by giving everyone three short directions, such as: "Run around the tree," "Jump over the stick," "Skip back to me." Add a new direction and do it again. Once you get to six tasks, consider pairing your family up to work at accomplishing the goal with two people's brain power!
• Search the internet for "Fun Following Directions Games." There are lots of great games for all ages!
• Watch "The Hiding Place" this week or next.

W E E K E I G H T

Begin with Prayer

Read Scripture:
Read Nehemiah 1:5, Matthew 22:37-38 and John 13:35.

Worship:
Sing hymns and/or worship songs
Share memorized verses

Family Discussion Questions:
What is a command?
(A direction or order)

Who loved first? Did God love us, or did we love God?
(God loved us first, 1 John 4:19)

What did God do because of His love for us, according to 1 John 4:9-10?
(God sent His son to be a payment, propitiation, for our sins.)

Why should we love other people?
(God loved us so we should love others, 1 John 4:11)

Ask if anyone has a personal prayer need that the rest of the family can pray for this week.

Bible Memory Recommendation (for upcoming week):
2 Corinthians 5:14-15, Ephesians 5:1-4

Close:
Read 2 Corinthians 5:14-15 and Ephesians 5:1-4.
Close in prayer as a family by going around the circle, first in Adoration, then Confession, then Thanksgiving, and concluding with Supplication.

WEEK NINE

"GET READY!"

Prepare: Complete the Senior Sword Study Week 9 **OR** read 1 John 4.

Write: Finish writing 1 John 4 in your "My Copy of 1 John" section and mark any references to God in Chapter 4.

Quick Notes: **Love**. God's love was the one and only focus for Week 9 of the 1 John Sword Study. Students looked at the four Greek words that represent *love*. Agape *love* is the *love* that John uses over and over in this small letter. Everyone marked the word *love* throughout the book with either a red colored pencil or a heart symbol.

Summary: 1 John 4 relays a crucial truth regarding love. The Greek word for God's love is *agape*. This type of love is different from all the others in that it is a compassionate, unconditional love. God's love is self-sacrificing versus a "when I feel like it" emotion, physical affection or friendship. This love is from the perspective of the giver displaying what is needed by the recipient. Thus, we see God, the Father, giving His Son as a payment for man's sins while man was still a sinner, an enemy. God's love saved us sacrificially. Now, through His power, He calls us to love others in the same manner, which will result in the world seeing Him. Thus, we chose 1 John 4:10 as the key verse.

Creative Family Ideas for the weekend – Theme: "Love"

- Bring supplies to create anonymous "love" notes to family and friends. Mail your cards after your Family Bonfire!

- Show your family's love to another family by coming up with a special gift of love. Bake a meal, clean a house or care for a lawn as a family.

- Bake bread for the elderly.

- Offer to care for the children of another family. Give the parents a gift card for dinner and send them on a date night.

- Regardless of the month, have a Valentine's Party!

- As a family, place old pennies, one per family member, in vinegar at this week's Family Bonfire in preparation for your Week 10 Bonfire.

- Consider purchasing the DVD, "St. John in Exile" with Dean Jones.

W E E K   N I N E

Begin with Prayer

Read Scripture:
Read 1 Corinthians 13

Worship:
Sing hymns and/or worship songs
Share memorized verses

Family Discussion Questions:
What is phileo love?
(Brotherly, friendship love)

What is agape love?
(God-like love that is of the will, self-sacrificing, compassionate and unconditional)

What did God's love do for us?
(Sent His Son, Jesus, as payment for our sins, 1 John 4:10)

List some of the attributes of God's love *(agape)* that you find in 1 Corinthians 13.
(See 1 Corinthians 13 for a list)

Review the "Day 10 Diagram" and ask if there are any questions. Ask each family member to share his or her diagram.
(A completed Diagram is on the next page for your reference.)

Ask if anyone has a personal prayer need that the rest of the family can pray for this week.

Bible Memory Recommendation (for upcoming week):
1 John 5:13, Psalm 119:160

Close:
Read 1 John 5:13 and Psalm 119:160.
Close in prayer as a family by going around the circle first, in Adoration, then Confession, then Thanksgiving, and concluding with Supplication.

Title: God is Love
Key Verse: 1 John 4:10

Chapter: Four
: 1 John 4:7-10, Phil 3:8-11
2 Cor. 5:14-15, Eph. 5:1-4

Greek Words: Love
~~ Agape: God's Love, Unconditional
~~ Storgay; Parent
Eros: Marriage
~~ Phileo: Friend

• Darkness
• Antichrist
• False Prophets
• Haters of Brothers
• Liars

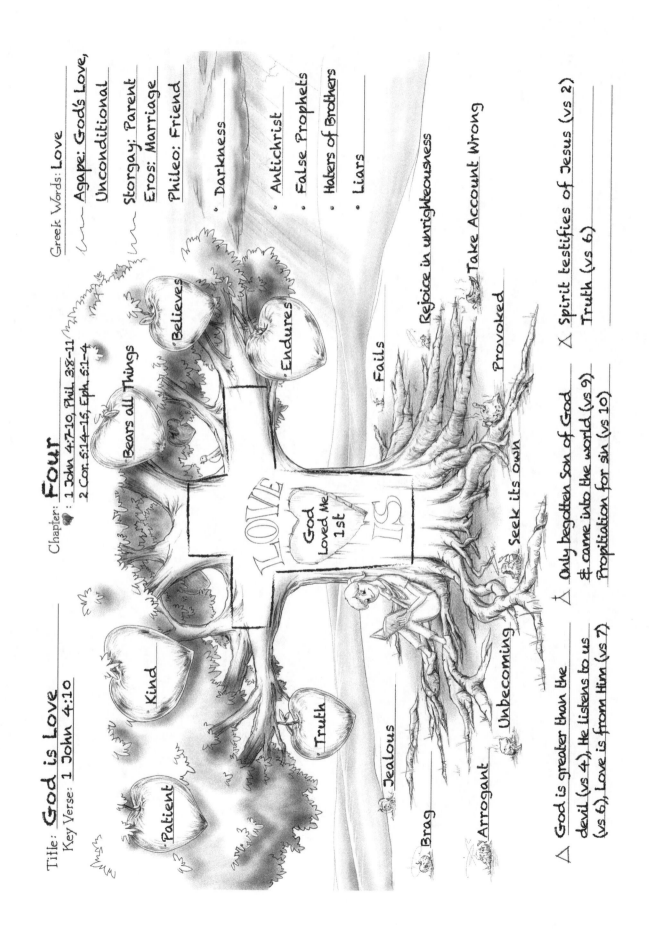

LOVE
God Loved Me 1st
IS

• Believes
• Endures
Bears all Things
• Kind
• Truth
• Patient

Fails
Jealous
Brag
Arrogant
Unbecoming
Seek its own
Provoked
Rejoice in unrighteousness
Take Account Wrong

△ God is greater than the devil (vs 4), He listens to us (vs 6), Love is from Him (vs 7)

△ Only begotten Son of God & came into the world (vs 9) Propitiation for sin (vs 10)

△ Spirit testifies of Jesus (vs 2) Truth (vs 6)

53

WEEK TEN

"GET READY!"

Prepare: Complete Senior Sword Study Week 10 **OR** read 1 John - read Chapter 5 twice.

Write: 1 John 5:1-13 is the writing task for this week.

Quick Notes: Everyone rounded the corner and headed for home this week as they dug into the final chapter of 1 John. Day 1 began with interviewing the chapter using the 5 W's and H. From their questioning, they found that John presented three witnesses of Jesus' deity: the Spirit, water and blood. The students spent three days looking at baptism and the power of Christ's death. Finally, they concluded the week looking at the attributes of liars and truth since John has mentioned both throughout the book of 1 John. We chose 1 John 5:13 as the key verse.

Summary: During the Levitical times, a person had to present two to three witnesses to prove a case against another. John moves from a call to love God, to our ability as His children to overcome the world through our belief in Jesus. Once again, John circles back to a previous point. His initial verses proclaimed his personal witness of Jesus. In Chapter 5, he proclaims even better witnesses for his defense of Jesus' presence on earth as God's Son. Even better, they witness that those who believe in Jesus as the Word of Life, will receive eternal life. Jesus is God and in Him there is eternal life - this is truth. Thus, he closes his debate with the Gnostic, false prophets. John has made his case, a true repetition of the Gospel, which was a message from Jesus Himself. Jesus is the way, the truth and the life. No man will come to the Father except through Jesus.

Creative Family Ideas for the weekend – Theme: "Washing & Cleaning"

• Pull out some tarnished silverware and polish it.

• Note the differences in your pennies from last week.

• Do tie-dyed shirts, talk about how the white under the rubberbands stays clean.

• Go on a street evangelizing trip as a family.

• Watch Ray Comfort's "Roots" series.

• Discuss baptism. Give an opportunity for any members who haven't been baptized to do so.

W E E K   T E N

Begin with Prayer

Read Scripture:
 Read John 14 and Psalm 51:5-7

Worship:
Sing hymns and/or worship songs
Share memorized verses

Family Discussion Questions:
 Who overcomes the world?
 (Those that believe in Jesus overcome the world, 1 John 5:5)

 What are the three witnesses?
 (The Spirit, the water and the blood, 1 John 5:8)

 What does baptism symbolize? What does it declare?
 (Baptism symbolizes the washing away of sins and the commitment, with the Spirit's help, to die to self and one's past. Baptism is also a public declaration of new life and a relationship with God through belief in Jesus Christ.)

 What is prayer?
 (Talking to God.)

 How do we know that God hears our prayers?
 (We know that if we ask according to His will, He hears us, 1 John 5:14)

 What is the final warning of 1 John?
 (We are to guard ourselves from idols, 1 John 5:21)

 Ask if anyone has a personal prayer need that the rest of the family can pray for this week.

Bible Memory Recommendation (for upcoming week):
 Romans 4:7-8, Matthew 22:36-40

Close:
Read Romans 4:7-8 and Matthew 22:36-40.
Close in prayer as a family by going around the circle, first in Adoration, then Confession, then Thanksgiving, and concluding with Supplication.

WEEK ELEVEN

"GET READY!"

Prepare: Complete Senior Sword Study Week 11 **OR** read 1 John and mark any references to God in Chapter 5.

Write: Finish copying the final verses of 1 John 5.

Quick Notes: All levels wrapped up their Sword Study of 1 John with word studies of *believe* and *understanding*. These two words in the Greek were not chosen for their repetitive nature, but for their importance to John's letter. They were a part of his summary statements to his readers: "Believe in Jesus, He will give you understanding." After learning the definitions, the students cemented their understanding of the Greek words through cross reference exercises.

Summary: As we come to the conclusion of 1 John, we hear our fatherly teacher summarize his message, once again: "Children of God, you know God because you believe in His Son, Jesus. Jesus will give you knowledge and understanding. You have eternal life through your faith in His work on the cross." The truth of his message resounds through the pages of 1 John to us just as it did to the readers of his day. As children of God, we have an intimate relationship with Jesus that gives us fellowship with the Father, love for others and a walk that abides with and models our Savior.

Creative Family Ideas for the weekend – Theme: "Believe... Have Faith!"

• Find and paint rocks with the word "Believe" or "Faith." Then, decorate your garden or flower beds with them as a reminder of your relationship with God through Jesus.

• Play games that require trust, such as Follow-the-Leader with a twist - blindfold all the members of your family, except the leader!

• Purchase a Scritpure wall stencil to place in prominent location in your home to proclaim your families faith in Christ.

• Make an acrostic for the word "believe."

W E E K   E L E V E N

Begin with Prayer

Read Scripture:
Read Psalm 36:5-10 and Romans 4:7-8

Worship:
Sing hymns and/or worship songs
Share memorized verses

Family Discussion Questions:
What must we believe to be a child of God?
(We must believe that Jesus is the Christ, 1 John 5:1)

What does the word believe mean?
(To have faith in or entrust one's spiritual well-being in Christ)

What does the word faith mean?
(Conviction or belief ... Christians have reliance on Christ for salvation)

If we believe in Jesus, what can we know that we have from God, the Father?
(Eternal life, 1 John 5:13)

Review the "Day 10 Diagram" and ask if there are any questions. Ask each family member to share his or her diagram.
(A completed Diagram is on the next page for your reference.)

Ask if anyone has a personal prayer need that the rest of the family can pray for this week.

Bible Memory Recommendation (for upcoming week):
Matthew 5:14-16, Hosea 6:3-6

Close:
Read Matthew 5:14-16 and Hosea 6:3-6.
Close in prayer as a family by going around the circle, first in Adoration, then Confession, then Thanksgiving, and concluding with Supplication.

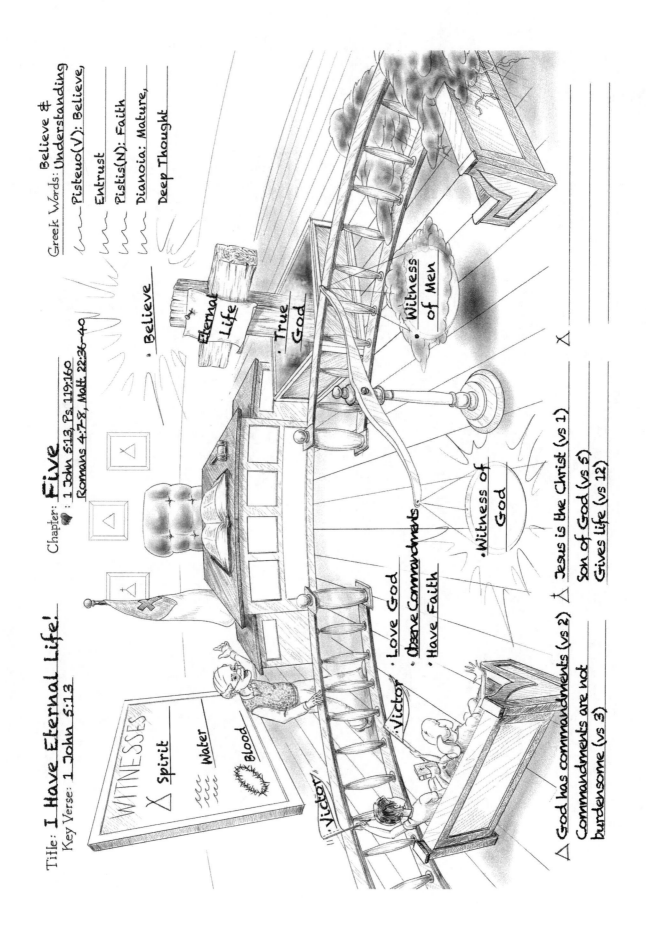

W E E K   T W E L V E

"GET READY!"

Prepare: Complete Senior Sword Study Week 12 **OR** read 1 John.

Quick Notes: Having completed the in-depth study of 1 John, students have spent the week refreshing their memories of each chapter's details by completing blank copies of the five Day 10 Diagrams. They have looked back at their prayer notes to see all that the Lord has taught them through their study of 1 John.

Creative Family Ideas for the weekend – Theme: "Washing & Cleaning"

• Watch the DVD, "St. John in Exile," with Dean Jones.

• Plan to have a mock Bible Bee using your 1 John Bible Memory Cards at your upcoming weekend Family Bonfire. All you need is a table with two chairs for the "official Judges," and chairs for the audience at the back of your room. Each child can take turns saying a memory passage.

• You could invite family and friends over for some fellowship and Bible Memory pres entations!

• Consider participating in the National Bible Bee with your family next summer. The event is sponsored by The Shelby Kennedy Foundation, and encourages and equips fami lies to deepen their relationships with Christ through God's Word. Plus, it's a lot of fun with fellow followers of Jesus!

W E E K   T W E L V E

Begin with Prayer

Read Scripture:
Read Psalm 111 and Jeremiah 9:23-24

Worship:
Sing hymns and/or worship songs
Share memorized verses

Family Discussion Questions:

What do you remember about John? *(Fisherman, Son of Zebedee, Brother to James, Matthew 4:17-24; Disciple of Jesus Christ, Matthew 10:1-2; Present with Jesus during transfiguration, Mark 9:1-2; Part of Jesus' inner circle, close friend, Mark 14:31-41; Prisoner on Patmos and Bondservant of God, Revelation 1:1, 9-11)*

John made two comparisons in 1 John 1; he compared light with _____ and truth with _____? *(Light to darkness, 1 John 1:5 and Truth to lie, 1 John 1:6)*

What is sin? *(An action against God's rules)*

Who has sinned? *(Everyone has sinned, Romans 3:23)*

What are some of the titles that John used for his recipients? *(Little children, Fathers, Young men, Beloved)*

Why do we need propitiation from God? *(Our sins, 1 John 2:2)*

What does the word *abide* **mean?** *(To dwell, live, remain with another in mind, heart and will)*

Because God loves us so much, what does He call us? *(His children, 1 John 3:1)*

What is the definition of righteous? *(Doing what is right according to God's rules)*

Who loved first? Did God love us, or did we love God? *(God loved us first, 1 John 4:19)*

What is *agape* **love?** *(God-like love that is of the will, self-sacrificing, compassionate and unconditional)*

What did God's love do for us? *(Sent His Son, Jesus, as payment for our sins, 1 John 4:10)*

Ask if anyone has a personal prayer need that the rest of the family can pray for this week.

Bible Memory Recommendation:
Review your Bible Memory Passages in some unique way.

Close: Read Psalm 51:1-10
Close in prayer as a family by going around the circle first, in Adoration, then Confession, then Thanksgiving, and concluding with Supplication.

STUDY OF 1 JOHN
A 12-Week Discipleship Study

Written by
Tammy McMahan

Illustrations by
Doug McGuire

Vignettes by
Marti Pieper

CONTENTS

FOCUS SCRIPTURES

"Thus says the LORD, "Let not a wise man boast of his wisdom, and let not the mighty man boast of his might, let not a rich man boast of his riches; but let him who boasts boast of this, that he understands and knows Me, that I am the LORD who exercises lovingkindness, justice and righteousness on earth; for I delight in these THINGS," DECLARES THE LORD."

Jeremiah 9:23-24
New American Standard Bible

"These things have I written unto you that believe on the name of the Son of God; that ye may know that ye have eternal life, and that ye may believe on the name of the Son of God."

1 John 5:13
King James Version

The Visitor

"Mmmmm, I love making cookies!" Melanie said as she watched her older sister stir the butter and brown sugar together in the bright blue mixing bowl.

"Don't you mean you love eating them?" Andrew chimed in as he looked up from his algebra. "Karissa's doing all the work."

"I love eating them best," Melanie grinned. "But making them is fun, too."

"Is that so?" Karissa smiled as she passed the bowl to her sister. "How about if you take a turn?"

"Thanks for working together, you two," Mom said as she entered the room with a loaded laundry basket in her arms. "We need the cookies wrapped and ready by 2:00."

"2:00?" Andrew paused again. "What's so special about 2:00?"

"Don't you remember? The UPS man always comes after that time," Karissa reminded her brother. "We're making a plate of cookies just for him."

"That's right," Melanie added. "The Bible Bee boxes went out two days ago, and Dad says they'll be here today. I can't wait to get our new Sword Studies!"

"Oh, I get it!" Andrew nodded. "Cookies make a great way to say 'thanks' to the UPS man. Say, I could use a little thank-you message, too!"

"I don't know why we're thanking you, but I'm sure you'll get plenty of cookies," Karissa said, dropping spoonfuls of dough onto the pan.

"For being the best big brother ever, of course!"

"Best—and only," Melanie commented. "But hurry, we need to get this pan in the oven! And Andrew, after you win that $100,000 top Senior Division prize at Bible Bee Nationals, you can buy all the cookies you want."

"For sure!" Karissa said. "You can even pay us to make them. But since we're going to win, too, we may not need the money."

"Wait a minute," a deep voice interrupted the friendly discussion. There in the kitchen stood a bearded, white-haired man dressed in a rough robe and sandals. "Aren't you three forgetting something?"

"Wait—what?" Andrew was the first to stutter out a response. "Who are you? *What* are you?"

"I'm the apostle John, author of the book you'll study for the next twelve weeks."

"Yeah, right," Melanie said, suspicion bathing her voice. "Dad? Are you trying to trick us again?"

Karissa stared, silent. One hand held a spoonful of cookie dough suspended over the pan.

"You may not believe this, but I really *am* the apostle John," the visitor continued. "They don't let me visit very often. But I thought you might need a dose of encouragement."

"Dose of encouragement?" said Melanie. "How about 'dose of sheer terror'? Did we go to sleep and wake up in *Adventures in Odyssey*?"

"Not at all," John reassured her. "Your guardian angels and I just wanted to assure you of the importance of what you are going to learn this summer. I can only stay a few minutes, but believe me, there's a lot more to the Bible Bee than the cash awards. May I tell you about this year's Sword Study?"

"Go ahead," said Karissa, slipping the pan of cookies into the oven.

John's brown eyes shone with excitement. "First of all, do you know what book we'll cover this year?"

"Our boxes haven't come yet, so no, we don't know," answered Melanie.

"All the more reason for me to tell you about my book."

"Your book? We must be studying the Gospel of John!"

"Not so fast, little sister," John cautioned. "I wrote more than one New Testament book. You remember that, don't you?"

Karissa nodded. "I know I do! You wrote the Gospel of John, but you also wrote the last book of the New Testament: Revelation."

"And let's not forget the others," added Andrew. "1 John, 2 John and 3 John. They're tiny, but mighty."

"Exactly!" John smiled at his new friends. "You've got it. Our focal book is the little one you call '1 John.' It's one of my favorites."

"1 John!" exclaimed Andrew. "Nothing to it!"

"Oh, you might be surprised," the apostle responded. "Like any good author, I know how to pack plenty of truth in a few words."

"But isn't 1 John like, umm, a letter or something?" asked Melanie. "No wonder it's so short."

You're right," John said. "This book isn't very long. It only has five little chapters, but holds essential truths that are far more valuable than any monetary prize. As you investigate each chapter deeply through your Sword Studies, you'll learn how you can know and follow God better in your lives today, though initially, I wrote it for my friends."

"Your friends?" Karissa asked. "Like some of the other apostles?"

"Not quite," John responded. "In this case, the 'friend' was a church—actually, several churches. I wrote the letter as a warning."

"A warning?" Andrew wrinkled his forehead.

"I wanted to warn my friends. We didn't have the Internet, but we still had lots of false teaching. Some people were saying Jesus wasn't God!" John sighed. "I wrote my book so my friends could know the truth."

"*Know the truth,*" Melanie said. "Mom's always saying that. And here she comes!"

In that instant, John disappeared. "Do you have the cookies done?" Mom asked, opening the door leading from the basement. "I can hardly wait for those boxes to arrive. And I love the way the Sword Study lets us all study the same thing at the same time."

"I do, too!" Melanie answered. "I bet the apostle John has all kinds of things to teach us!"

"The apostle John—but how . . . did the UPS driver already come?"

"Not yet. But you know me. I just want to know the truth." Melanie paused with a knowing look at her siblings. "And this time, I have a feeling it'll come through the apostle John. Hurry! I think I hear the delivery truck now!"

(to be continued)

DAY ONE

ON MY KNEES:

Greetings! Welcome friend, new or old, to the book of 1 John. You are about to begin studying an amazing book of the Bible. Can you say, "Confidence?" In a world where doubt, confusion and questions abound, 1 John declares "Assurance," with a capital "A!" This book is perfect for you at such a time as this.

As you begin, our prayer is that the Sword Study format will help guide you in diligent study of God's Word. The process of allowing "Scripture to answer Scripture" is central to deepening your personal relationship with the Lord.

Daily, the ON YOUR KNEES portion of your study will strive to prepare your heart for the INVESTIGATIVE STUDY of 1 John by guiding you in prayerful preparation through writing and reading of Scripture. Keys to being able to focus and hear from the Lord without distraction are to create a specific time and place for your study, and to have your Bible and a pencil nearby. Once you are all organized, let's begin in prayer.

Pray. "Assurance. Confidence. Absolutes without doubt. Lord, You are the Author of all things. You are the beginning and the end. As I begin my study of 1 John, open my ears and eyes to Your Word and the confidence that only You can give me as I strive to know You more. In Your Son Jesus' name, I pray. Amen."

Write. As we look at 1 John from an AERIAL VIEW, we will be writing passages that encourage us to fellowship with the Lord. Turn to Psalm 145:18-19 and hear what happens when we call out to the Lord! _____

_____

_____

_____

Read. Each day this week, before you will begin the INVESTIGATIVE STUDY portion of your Sword Study, you will read the entire book of 1 John. This task may seem laborious, but it will help provide you with familiartiy and a solid foundation for understanding the book. Take the time to read all of the chapters in one sitting. Reading aloud can help slow your pace. The goal is not to dissect and interpret what you are reading at this point, so don't get caught up in what the words mean or allow your mind to wander by trying to figure out how to apply what you read. Please read 1 John now.

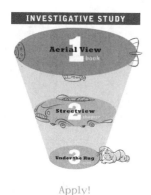

INVESTIGATIVE STUDY
AERIAL

      Our initial view of 1 John this week will be from a high altitude. Continually remind yourself to stay out of the details and remain focused on the big picture. Answer the following questions by recollection or by quickly skimming back over the text.

What type of literature is 1 John? _____

What word or words stood out to you as you read 1 John?

_____

What were some of the features of his writing style that you noticed?

_____

APPLY!

"Iron sharpens iron, and one man sharpens another."
~ Proverbs 27:17 ESV ~

      Once or twice a week, you will find an "Apply" section that will include a simple activity that gives you the opportunity to live out what you have learned through your week's study.

      Who among your family and friends would be a good accountability partner? Think through those you know and choose someone who you could ask to check in with you to see how you are doing with your daily time in the Sword Study. Ideally, it would be someone that you could help keep accountable to their own Sword Study! Give that person a call, or write him or her an e-mail. Ask your partner to check in with you each week to ask what you have learned, and perhaps listen to you recite one of your recommended Bible memory passages.

A.C.T.S. PRAYER TIME

      At the end of each day's INVESTIGATIVE STUDY section, we will use this A.C.T.S. PRAYER TIME section to pray for strength to live out what we have heard through His Word.

      We will use the A.C.T.S. prayer model by beginning in *Adoration* of who God is. Next, we will admit or *Confess* to Him where we know that we are falling short. *Confessing* the things that He brings to our attention paves the way for a clear conscience and uninhibited fellowship with Him. Follow with a time of gratitude, *Thanking* Him for all you have been shown through your study and finish by bringing any requests *(Supplications)* to accomplish what you have learned from Him. For the next several weeks, we will give you "prayer starters" as examples of how you could interact with God using the A.C.T.S. model.

A– "Jesus, Word of Life, Provider of eternal life and fellowship, You are awesome and mighty. I stand in awe of Your example. I want to walk in the light as You did while you were on earth. In Your strength and power I am able to conquer all things."

C – "Lord, I confess that I do not always depend upon You and follow Your example. I make decisions and do things before even considering how You would want me to act."

T – "Thank you for showing me lovingkindness and patience as You gently train me in the ways of Your Father."

S – "Help me to stop and think before acting. Cause me to pause and purposefully consider Your thoughts on my actions, reactions and options. I want to grow in my ability to do the right thing and walk the right way. Doing a study every day can be a challenge for me, so please give me the desire to do it faithfully."

"The Bible is not an end in itself, but a means to bring men to an intimate and satisfying knowledge of God, that they may enter into Him, that they may delight in His Presence, may taste and know the inner sweetness of the very God Himself in the core and center of their hearts."
~ A. W. Tozer ~

DIGGING DEEPER

Occasionally, you may find a "DIGGING DEEPER" section after the A.C.T.S. Prayer Time. Do not feel pressured to do this section, or feel that you have not completed your study if you don't do the suggested activity.

The additional material in this section comes from the "cutting room floor." While we would have liked to include what is found here in the core Sword Study, it simply would have made the day's time commitment too long. Should you find yourself zipping through the day or with extra time at the end of the week, going back to a DIGGING DEEPER section would be time well spent.

D A Y   T W O

ON MY KNEES:

Come. Join us again at the feet of Jesus. His words are all we need. By coming to Him for wisdom, our days will start in a right way, lit by His insights and prepared for His lessons. We will be able to attack our days and undergo trials in His strength if His words are resounding in our thoughts.

Pray. "Jesus, you are my patient teacher. I want to listen intently to Your words. I want to look into Your Textbook of textbooks and be a diligent student. Keep my mind focused and heart open to all You have for me today."

Write. On the lines below, write Isaiah 26:3-4. _____

_____

_____

_____

_____

Read. Settle in and read the entire book of 1 John again. Do not grow weary in this process; you will be amazed at how quickly John's words will sound familiar.

Apply!

INVESTIGATIVE STUDY
AERIAL

The book of 1 John begins a little differently than the "normal" epistles, particularly those of Paul. Since Paul wrote so many of the New Testament books and letters, many of us have grown accustomed to his greetings and announcements of authorship. In 1 John, we may find ourselves asking, "Where is the warm greeting?" or, "Where is the salutation revealing the author?" You may wonder, "Who starts a letter mid-thought?!"

Historical and traditional authorship of 1 John has been attributed to John, the son of Zebedee. 1 John's content and language style are very similar to John's other books: the Gospel of John, 2 John, 3 John and Revelation.

Many historians believe that John wrote this letter later in his life between 96 to 99 A.D. John had lived in Ephesus since the period when Jerusalem fell to the Romans in A.D. 70. Find and mark Ephesus on the map below.

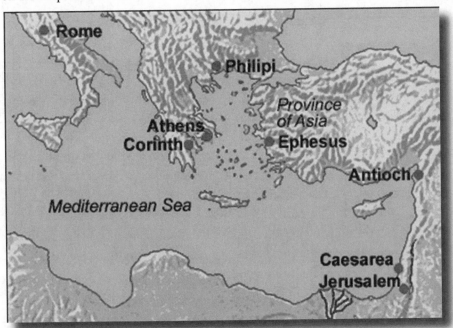

Ephesus was a wealthy shipping port and the capital city of the Roman province of Asia. This is where modern-day Turkey is located. The lay of the land included forests in the south and orchards in the east. The sea was to the west and fields characterized the north. One of the Seven Wonders of the Ancient World, the extravagant temple of Artemis/Diana, was a focal point of idolatry during the time period in which John wrote his letter. Quickly look at how the town clerk described Ephesus in Acts 19:35. Note what you find here:

_____

Since John gets right to the point of his message and doesn't take the time or effort to give us details about himself, we will look at other passages around the New Testament to get to know the man whom God inspired to write His words.

Note what you learn about John on the lines after each passage.

Matthew 4:21 _____

_____

Matthew 10:1-2 _____

_____

Mark 9:1-2 _____

Mark 14:32-34 _____

Revelation 1:1-2, 9-11 _____

_____

_____

From the book's title, we accept John to be the author. To whom is he referring when he says "we" throughout his letter? _____

Today, we have learned that John was a fisherman and among the first disciples that Jesus asked to join Him in ministry. Through the gospels, we can observe how John drew near to Jesus as time passed. He was one of Jesus' closest, earthly friends...a part of His inner circle. John was invited to pray with Jesus in the dark hours before His death. Jesus cried out to him from the cross to care for His dear, earthly mom (John 19:25). John was a part of Jesus' earthly and spiritual family. How special this letter will become to us, if we allow the Spirit to teach us its message of sweet fellowship and joy in our relationship with Jesus, His Father and the family of Believers!

A.C.T.S. PRAYER TIME

How are you doing? During these first days, you may find that looking at the "facts and figures" of 1 John seems tedious, or you may find investigating John's background to be a new revelation. Either way, whenever we dig into the Word of God, He promises blessings to us. We pray that as you read through the chapters of 1 John, peruse the Scripture for details about John and desire to learn more of God's character, you will be encouraged and refreshed in your relationship with the Eternal, One and Only God. Close your fellowship time with Him in prayer.

A – "Lord, You are so good to me, all the time. You know my heart of doubt and lack of understanding. You knew that showing me real men with real faults in the Bible would make it easier for me to understand. Seeing Your love and patience with them gives me a better picture of how You do the same with me."

C – "Lord, I confess that I don't always feel like spending time in Your Word. I am so used to being entertained and to having information easily accessible without needing to work to learn. Give me endurance and the desire to be with You."

T – "Thank You, Lord that I can admit my faults and how I really feel without You deserting me or thinking less of me ."

S – "Lord, bring Your Word alive to me even when I come in obedience, but without excitement. Help me look forward to this time with increasing desire every day."

"You may as well quit reading and hearing the Word of God, and give it to the devil, if you do not desire to live according to it."
~ Martin Luther ~

DIGGING DEEPER

John was one of the twelve disciples that Jesus chose. Using a Bible dictionary, find the definition of a "disciple" and note what you find here: _____

_____

Do you consider yourself as a disciple of Jesus according to the general definition? _____

Who were the other 11 disciples? List them here and note something about each one. (Use Matthew 10 as a starting point)

DISCIPLE	NOTES

DAY THREE

ON MY KNEES:

Day 3. You are doing well! Each time you return to His feet, He promises to bless you. He has set eternity in the hearts of all people. When we come to Him to learn, He fills the void within our hearts. Let's return to Him in prayer before beginning to look at the false beliefs of John's day.

Pray. "Lord, I know You are near me when I call out to You. I know that my heart is deceitful, so I am coming to You for truth. Hear my cry for wisdom. Teach me more of Your holiness and abundant life so that I might grow in maturity through Your strength."

Write. Turn to Psalm 111:7-10* and carefully read the words. Can you hear His words confirming your time of study? Write verse 10 on the lines below and commit them to memory, as soon as you are able, as a reminder of His promises to YOU. _____

_____

_____

_____

Read. Once again, please read 1 John.

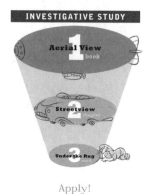

Apply!

INVESTIGATIVE STUDY
AERIAL

A crucial part of your AERIAL VIEW observations is gaining an understanding of the historical times and context of the book you are studying. While we learned that the temple of Artemis/Diana, the goddess of fertility, was a centerpiece of Ephesus, a greater threat to Christianity arose in the background of John's writing. Whenever error is mixed with truth, discernment becomes more difficult. The churches of John's day were under the attack of a false teaching called Gnosticism.

Using a paper or online dictionary, write a simple definition of Gnosticism on the lines below:

_____

_____

_____

The Webster's 1913 Dictionary defines a Gnostic as "a knowing, wise, shrewd man that claims to have a deeper wisdom."

The multi-faceted splinters of Gnosticism make it difficult to understand each claim. The Gnostic claimed a person just wasn't spiritually enlightened or knowledgeable if they didn't understand an aspect of their thinking. Here are some of the main points of Gnosticism; beneath each is a counter argument, a Biblical defense. After studying the entire letter of 1 John, it will be even more interesting to see how John dealt with each of these wayward beliefs.

1. God is a spirit that does not and cannot actually do anything in the physical world. So, if he wants to accomplish anything he has to operate through angels and demons.

In contradiction, the Word of God in 1 Timothy 3:16 says: _____
_____

2. Thus, according to the Gnostic, God is distant and aloof without a desire for fellowship with men.

In contradiction, the Word of God in Exodus 33:11-12 gives an example of close friendship when it says: _____
_____

3. The souls of men are little pieces of God that want to get back to Him, so to be "saved" one has to escape their flesh through mental knowledge.

In contradiction, the Word of God in Acts 16:30-31 says: _____
_____

4. Dualism, the belief that good and evil exist side by side battling for dominance, is a part of Gnosticism. Dualism states that neither side will win because everything has a little bit of good and a little bit of bad. The yin-yang symbolizes dualism.

In contradiction, the Word of God says in Mark 10:18 that only one is good:
_____
_____

5. Gnostics place extreme emphasis on receiving a deeper, secret knowledge. Thus, their name came from the Greek word for knowledge, gnosis.

In contradiction, the Word of God in Acts 4:13 says: _____
_____

Many of these beliefs caused false teachers to propagate heresies that righteousness was not a duty of the Christian life and that Christ was not God incarnate. Some teachers denied the humanity of Jesus and others denied His deity. As we study 1 John we will quickly recognize how the Gnostic heresies affected John's purposes in writing to his recipients, and to us. Surely, we will see him show believers how they can fellowship with God, and that the "uneducated" and "untrained" man can be enlightened to salvation!

A.C.T.S. PRAYER TIME

"So that thou incline thine ear unto wisdom, and apply thine heart to understanding;
Yea, if thou criest after knowledge, and liftest up thy voice for understanding;
If thou seekest her as silver, and searchest for her as for hid treasures;
Then shalt thou understand the fear of the Lord, and find the knowledge of God.
For the Lord giveth wisdom: out of his mouth cometh knowledge and understanding."
~ Proverbs 2:2-6 KJV ~

When confusion and lack of clarity stir in your heart be sure to go to the Provider of Wisdom. As we come to close of our study, particularly of the false teachings of John's time, we need to remember our plumb line. We gain truth and wisdom from the One and Only God of heaven and earth. Go to Him in prayer using Proverbs 2:2-6 as a guide.

A - "Praise You, God, for You are the giver of all wisdom. How good it is to know that You preserve my way and provide knowledge that is pleasant to my soul. So often, man's knowledge is confused and brings strife to my soul."

C - "God, I admit that sometimes I seek man's knowledge and rely on it for my decisions. I want to go to You for knowledge and understanding."

T - "Thank You for guarding my path and preserving me."

S - "I want to discern righteousness, justice and follow Your good course. Show me how, Lord; I want to follow You and fellowship deeply as my normal way of life."

"Here, then, is the real problem of our negligence. We fail in our duty to study God's Word not so much because it is difficult to understand, not so much because it is dull and boring, but because it is work. Our problem is not a lack of intelligence or a lack of passion. Our problem is that we are lazy."
~ R. C. Sproul ~

DAY FOUR

ON MY KNEES:

Are you ready to jump right back into your study? First, go to the Lord in prayer so that you put yourself under His guidance instead of potentially reading into things with your own perspective. Pray for His words to drown out your thoughts and interpretations.

Pray. "Lord, it is true- I can read into Your words based on what my heart wants to hear. Help me to slow down and simply read in a way that opens my heart and mind to Your meanings and applications. Take away the calls to hurry through the details that don't interest me. Close out the noise of my other activities by placing a hedge around me during this time so I won't have any unnecessary interruptions to our time. I can't wait to see what You have to teach me today. In Jesus' name, I pray, amen."

Write. Turn to Psalm 119:159-160 and read the Scripture passage. Prayerfully write it on lines below.

_____

_____

_____

_____

Read. The effort that it takes to read 1 John in its entirety is well worth your time. Consider the special letters or emails that you receive from loved ones. You read them over and over. They are evaluated word by word. Cherished and re-read throughout the day. You are reading a letter inspired by the Almighty, Creator God. Soak up His letter to you as you read 1 John again today!

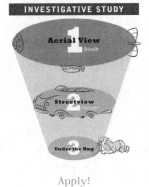

INVESTIGATIVE STUDY

Aerial View
book

Streetview

Under the Rug

Apply!

INVESTIGATIVE STUDY
AERIAL

A trademark of John's letter is his "these things I write" statements. There are seven in all. Today, we will locate them in our Bibles, mark them with a pencil symbol and then write them out on the lines below. Tomorrow, we will use them to make our own temporary titles for the book of 1 John.

Chapter 1, Verse 4: _____

Chapter 2, Verse 1: _____

🖎   Chapter 2, Verse 12: _____

🖎   Chapter 2, Verse 13: _____

_____

🖎   Chapter 2, Verse 14: _____

_____

🖎   Chapter 2, Verse 21: _____

🖎   Chapter 2, Verse 26: _____

🖎   Chapter 5, Verse 13: _____

Did you see an underlying defense against the false teachers of Gnosticism as you wrote each of John's reasons for writing? As we continue to dig deeper into this short epistle, we will see John proclaim, "You can fellowship with God, through His Son Jesus! God is not just a spirit; I saw Him, fellowshipped with Him and worked with Him!" John will describe how sin affects fellowship, how false teachers will undermine confidence of your fellowship, and how to fellowship with other believers, God and Jesus. What an exciting book to spend our time investigating!

A . C . T . S .   P R A Y E R   T I M E

"The LORD sat as King at the flood; yes, the LORD sits as King forever. The LORD will give strength to His people; The LORD will bless His people with peace."
~ Psalm 29:10-11 NASB ~

Come, let us **Adore** the Lord for surely He is deserving of our adoration above all. For He spoke the heavens and earth into existence, created all things for His glory and in His goodness. How awesome and good He is! He does not fret or pace in worry. He sits and rules! In humble **confession**, share the areas of this week that you tried to rule instead of giving Him the throne and lordship of your days. Praise and **give gratitude** to Him for the strength, blessings and peace that He lavishes on His people. **Ask** for confirmations of His blessings and eyes to see His answers.

A - "God, You are the King of kings, Lord of lords and my heavenly Father. You are amazing, beyond my highest thoughts. When the world seems out of control due to weather or man, You sit in the high places in control."

C - "Oh, I confess that I do not always recognize and give you honor as the Ruler of my life. I fret and worry over a variety of things in my life, showing a lack of trust and belief in Your words of Psalm 29."

T - "Even in my weaknesses and faults, You promise to bless me. Thank you, Lord. Thank You. I am so grateful for Your attention."

S - "Help me to recognize Your gifts today. I do not want to be ungrateful or grumble. I want to notice and praise You throughout the day for how You show Yourself to me."

"Righteousness and justice are the foundation of Your throne; Mercy and truth go before Your face. Blessed are the people who know the joyful sound! They walk, O Lord, in the light of Your countenance. In Your name they rejoice all day long, And in Your righteousness they are exalted."
~ Psalm 89:14-16 NKJV ~

DAY FIVE

ON MY KNEES:

Wow! Week 1 is coming to an end. The word of God is endless, new every morning and able to refine us for His glory. Keep in mind the great gift it is as we gain wisdom and knowledge on how to live in true peace. We have an awesome, loving, heavenly Father, for sure!

Pray. "Father, as I come before You to study Your Word, I desire to know You more, and I trust that You will help me to understand Your truth. Please fellowship with me today. In Jesus' name, I pray."

Write. Jeremiah 9:23-24* is a tremendous reminder that we are invited to fellowship with the King of kings and Lord of lords! On the lines below, write out these two verses. This passage is one of our Focus Scriptures for 1 John.

_____

_____

_____

_____

_____

_____

_____

Read. You've made it! One more time, read through the book of 1 John. It will be quite a while before we make this request of you again.

INVESTIGATIVE STUDY
AERIAL

INVESTIGATIVE STUDY

1 Aerial View *book*

2 Streetview *chapter*

3 Under the Rug

Apply!

We are about to wrap up our investigation from the big-picture level, but before we drop down to a more detailed look at 1 John, let's summarize your findings thus far.

Do this by temporarily titling each of the chapters and choosing what you would consider the key verse in each of them. There are no wrong answers here. Your personal titles for the chapters will help you remember what you have learned and initially observed.

Chapter 1 – Title _____

Chapter 1 – Key Verse (write it out!) _____

_____

_____

Chapter 1 – Summary Paragraph (no more than 2-3 sentences) _____

_____

_____

Chapter 2 – Title _____

Chapter 2 – Key Verse (write it out!) _____

_____

_____

Chapter 2 – Summary Paragraph (no more than 2-3 sentences) _____

_____

_____

Chapter 3 – Title _____

Chapter 3 – Key Verse (write it out!) _____

_____

_____

Chapter 3 – Summary Paragraph (no more than 2-3 sentences) _____

_____

_____

Chapter 4 – Title _____

Chapter 4 – Key Verse (write it out!) _____

_____

_____

Chapter 4 – Summary Paragraph (no more than 2-3 sentences) _____

_____

_____

Chapter 5 – Title _____

Chapter 5 – Key Verse (write it out!) _____

_____

_____

Chapter 5 – Summary Paragraph (no more than 2-3 sentences) _____

_____

_____

A.C.T.S. PRAYER TIME

"The fear of the LORD is the beginning of wisdom: a good understanding have all they that do his commandments: his praise endureth for ever."
~ Psalm 111:10 KJV ~

A - "Lord, You are trustworthy. You are an everlasting Rock. When others fail me or I fail You, You continue to be trustworthy and faithful."

C - "Forgive me, Lord, when I do not keep my mind on You and Your ways."

T - "How do I express my gratitude? I feel so unable to put my thanks in words for all You have done and continue to do on my behalf. I am so thankful that You know me and love me just the same."

S - "Please help me to keep my mind focused on You and Your ways as I walk through the rest of this day and throughout the rest of the weekend. I want to experience peace in all You have planned for me. Help me to be an example to those around me as well."

"The BIBLE -- banned, burned, beloved. More widely read, more frequently attacked than any other book in history. Generations of intellectuals have attempted to discredit it, dictators of every age have outlawed it and executed those who read it. Yet soldiers carry it into battle believing it more powerful than their weapons. Fragments of it smuggled into solitary prison cells have transformed ruthless killers into gentle saints."
~ Charles Colson ~

DIGGING DEEPER

0	10	20	30	40	50	60	70	80	90	100

Research and complete a timeline of John's life and ministry. Make sure to include important events such as his birth, call to be one of the twelve disciples and death. There are some differences of opinion among scholars, but general ranges of dates will be sufficient. You can investigate using your Logos software, Blue Letter Bible or a Bible Dictionary.

Dwight L. Moody: Light of Chicago

On January 14, 1870, three junior reporters from the River Oaks News Club had the privilege of interviewing Reverend Dwight L. Moody, one of our country's most well-known evangelists.

What's an evangelist? Our club wondered that, too, so we sent Alex Thomas (seventeen), Zachary Baker (fourteen) and Hunter Nelson (ten) over to Rev. Moody's office in downtown Chicago for some answers. Here's their interview:

Alex: Thanks so much for your time, sir. I know you agreed to meet with us because you like young people. Can you explain?

Moody: For one thing, young man, you should know I was once a young man, too, way back in Northfield, Massachusetts. Hard to believe, isn't it? Did you know I never went past the fifth grade? Stay with your education. It will serve you well.

Zachary: Why did you drop out of school, sir?

Moody: It wasn't a case of dropping out, my friend, but of helping support my family. You see, my father died when I was but four years old. Soon, my mother delivered twins, giving me seven siblings. Once I was strong enough to do a man's work on the farm, Mother urged me to quit school.

Hunter: Reverend Moody, I can't even imagine such hardship. Did you become a farmer?

Moody (*chuckles*) : Not for long, son, not for long. You see, I was better at talking to people than to cornstalks. By age seventeen, I said goodbye to the fields and hello to my uncle's shoe business in Boston. Even then, I was in the business of saving soles.

Alex *(laughing)* : We heard you had a good sense of humor, sir. Anyway, did you succeed in the shoe business?

Moody: I did well, tolerably well. In fact, I had a goal to become a millionaire. But God did better with me than I did in business.

Zachary: Can you explain, sir?

Moody: That's quite a story, my boy. As one of the requirements for my employment, Uncle Samuel insisted I attend his church. Reluctantly, I went. But before long, my Sunday School teacher, Edward Kimball, visited me in Uncle's shoe shop. He said, "I want to tell you how much Christ loves you." Right then, I knelt to receive Christ's love-gift of salvation and surrendered my soul to Him.

Hunter: Amazing! So is that when you first became a preacher and evangelist?

Moody: No, not quite. At that point, my mind was still more cluttered with dollars than doing God's will. About that time, I made the decision to move to the big city of Chicago. There, I fully intended to make my fortune in the shoe business.

Alex: And did you?

Moody: Praise God, He got hold of me before the money did. I rented a room from a woman I called Mother Phillips. She held me accountable to pray, read my Bible daily and attend church. She also asked me to assist her in city mission work. I began an outreach to the thousands of poor children who roamed Chicago's streets and alleys.

Zach: Is that how you became an evangelist? We've heard you called "the light of Chicago," but we don't quite understand.

Moody: Well, I bet you're an evangelist, too, my boy —

someone who shares the good news of Jesus Christ. That's how I shone my light for the Lord. I started volunteering for the local YMCA (Young Men's Christian Association) while still selling shoes. As my passion for the Lord and His work grew, I held more and more evangelistic meetings, concentrating especially on the youth.

Hunter: Yet people called you "Crazy Moody." Why?

Moody (laughing): I think that came about the time I held a Bible class beside Lake Michigan. The young people sat on driftwood to listen. Some would have called my actions "crazy," I suppose.

Zachary: What other ministries were you involved in, sir?

Moody: One of the first efforts I made became the foundation for the rest. In 1858, I started a mission Sunday School at North Market Hall in a slum of our fair city.

Hunter: I know what Sunday School is, but what's a "mission" Sunday School? And what's a slum?

Moody: You remind me of myself, young man. So much to learn, and so many questions. No one at the time knew what a mission Sunday School was, either. But some fellow church-goers promised to allow me to have a Sunday School class if I made my own. So I went out, like the disciples, into the highways and byways—only in my case, it was the alleys and street corners—and brought them in.

Hunter: Brought them in?

Moody: Yes, sir. I brought poor children, all from immigrant families, right into the church and gave them all the Bible teaching I could. And son, you asked about the word "slum." These children lived in places no one should ever have to live. But the first Sunday, eighteen of these children came with me to Sunday

School. And we did nothing but grow from there on out.

Alex: Your life was changing fast, wasn't it, sir?

Moody: Yes, indeed. In 1860, I left the business world forever, believing my life should not be spent piling up wealth but helping the less fortunate. Our Sunday School grew to more than 1500 people, and people began urging me to start a church. So on February 28, 1864, the Illinois Street Church opened with me as its pastor.

Even with all their questions, our reporters still haven't finished finding out about Reverend Moody. Stay tuned to next week's Sword Study as they continue their conversation.

D A Y   O N E

ON MY KNEES:

How often we come rushing into the day's events before coming to the Lord to hear from Him! Fellow student, as you come to study, pause in prayer first. Be still and know that He is God, for your day should revolve around Him, not vice versa. (Psalm 46)

Pray. "Father God, I am often in high speed, constantly going about the affairs of my day. I want to be undistracted. I want to be Yours and Yours alone while I am in Your Word. Help me hear Your thoughts and understand Your ways so that I might be a faithful child of Yours."

Write. We have come to a very special point. Today, you will begin writing your own copy of 1 John. Turn to the "Write!" section of your Sword Study and write 1 John 1:1.

Read. As we drop down for a closer view of 1 John, read only Chapter 1.

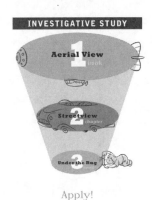

Apply!

INVESTIGATIVE STUDY
STREETVIEW: *CHAPTER 1*

Coming down from the heights of the AERIAL VIEW, we will take the next 10 days to fully investigate the first chapter of 1 John. There are so many details that hurrying through the passages or staying at a higher level would cause us to miss the depth of John's message. The Word of God is limitless and continuously able to reveal new knowledge to us.

Today, we will use an interview format to look at the chapter through quizzing the passages with "Who, What, Why, When, Where and How" questions. Use only the Scripture's words to answer the following questions. While it is tempting to write what we think, the goal is to hear from the Lord.

Verse 1

How long had the Word of Life been in existence? _____

_____

Circle the ways in which John said he knew the Word of Life:

Hearing   Seeing   Touching   Fellowshipping

According to John 1:1, Who is the Word of Life? _____

_____

Verse 2

What three things do we learn about the Word of Life in 1 John 1:2? _____
_____

Verse 3

What did John proclaim or declare regarding what he had seen and heard? _____
_____

With whom did John have fellowship, according to verse 3? _____
_____

Who is the Son of God? _____

Verse 4

Why did John write these things, according to 1 John 1:4? _____
_____

Verse 5

What was the message? _____

From whom did John hear the message? _____

What did he do with the message? _____

Verse 6

What are we, if we say we have fellowship with God, yet are walking in darkness?_____

What is true of us or the person who is not in fellowship with God? _____
_____

What is missing in our lives if we are walking in the darkness? _____
_____

Verse 7

Whose example are we following if we walk in the light? _____

What two things happen when we walk in the light? _____
_____

What power does the blood of Christ have, according to verse 7? _____

_____

Verse 8

How do we know if we are deceived and the truth isn't in us? _____

_____

Is it true that everyone sins, according to this verse? _____

Verse 9

What two things happen if we confess our sins? _____

_____

Who is the "He" in this verse? _____

What two characteristics of the Father are listed in this verse? _____

Verse 10

What two things are true if we say we have not sinned, according to this verse?

_____

_____

According to verse 6 and 10, who are the two possibilities of liars? _____

_____

A.C.T.S. PRAYER TIME

Bow in prayer before the Lord, sharing your *Adoration* for His Word of life. How amazing that He would send His Son, Jesus Christ, for man to hear, see and touch. *Confess* those sins that He has convicted you of as you were in His Word. Give Him *Thanksgiving* for showing you how to walk in His light and during your *Supplication* time, request that He would provide the strength, wisdom and endurance to walk in the light.

A –"God of light, I praise You for revealing Your Son to me."

C –"Father, I admit that I stumble at times and walk in my flesh."

T –"Thank you for giving me Your Spirit to empower me to walk in the light."

S –"God, help me to be quick to confess my sins."

"Some people like to read so many [Bible] chapters every day. I would not dissuade them from the practice, but I would rather lay my soul asoak in half a dozen verses all day than rinse my hand in several chapters. Oh, to be bathed in a text of Scripture, and to let it be sucked up in your very soul, till it saturates your heart!"
~ Charles Haddon Spurgeon ~

DIGGING DEEPER

There is so much to learn and understand about Jesus, the Word of Life. John went into great detail referring to Jesus as the Word in John 1:1-14. These passages also tie back to Genesis 1.

In the beginning: Gensis 1:1   John 1:1   1 John 1:1

Take a few minutes to read these passages and note all that you learn from them about Jesus.

_____

_____

_____

_____

_____

_____

D A Y   T W O

ON MY KNEES:

Come, faithful student of the Word. Are you settled in and ready to have your soul refreshed by the precepts of your God? Begin by going to your Heavenly Father in silent supplication.

Pray. "Father, hear me this morning as I come in adoration. I want to be refreshed and washed in Your Word today. Teach me new insights and give me Your strength, to live out what I learn. In Jesus' name, I pray, amen."

Write. Turn to the "My Copy of 1 John" section and prayerfully copy 1 John 1:2 on your page's lines.

Read. Once again, read 1 John 1 in its entirety before moving to the INVESTIGA-TIVE STUDY portion of your day.

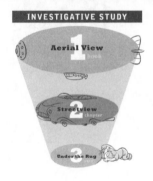

INVESTIGATIVE STUDY

Apply!

INVESTIGATIVE STUDY
STREETVIEW: CHAPTER 1

Another way to dig deeper into a chapter of verses is to look for lists and comparisons within the text. For the mind that likes patterns, this is helpful in better understanding the passage. There are several lists and a couple of comparisons in the first ten verses of 1 John.

Let's begin with the lists.

How the Word of Life Was Experienced, according to Verse 1

1. They _____ Him.

2. They _____ Him.

3. They _____ Him.

4. They _____ Him.

The Word of Life, according to Verses 1 & 2

1.   The Word of Life was: _____

2.   The Word of Life was: _____

3.   The Word of Life was: _____

4.   The Word of Life was: _____

5.   The Word of Life was: _____

What the Word of Life Provides, according to Verse 3

1.   Fellowship with: _____

2.   Fellowship with: _____

3.   Fellowship with: _____

Comparisons in Chapter 1

Light compared to: _____ (What verse in 1 John 1? _____)

Truth compared to: _____ (What verses in 1 John 1? _____)

List of "If... Then" Statements

1. Verse 6
If we: _____
But: _____
Then we: _____
And: _____

2. Verse 7
If we: _____
Then we: _____
And: _____

3. Verse 8
If we: _____
Then we: _____
And: _____

4. Verse 9

If we: _____

Then God: _____

And God: _____

5. Verse 10

If we: _____

Then we: _____

And: _____

APPLY!

Liar, liar, pants on fire!

Where did that childhood taunt come from? Well, it came from an 1810 poem by William Blake titled, "The Liar." Interesting that a political group called "Polifact" uses a scale to describe levels of truth (how is that possible?) in political reports by ranking items from "True" to "Pants on Fire."

A lie is described as "a false statement with the intent to deceive." As you looked at the five "if…then" statements, it becomes evident that what we **say** must be supported by what we **do**.

Take time to make an honest assessment of your walk by asking yourself the 1 John 1:6-10 questions below:

Am I in fellowship with the Lord right now? _____

Am I characterized by walking in the darkness in any area of my life? _____

Am I walking like Jesus? _____

Is there any sin I need to confess to restore my fellowship with God? _____

A.C.T.S. PRAYER TIME

Praise the Lord, He has revealed eternal life through His Son, Jesus Christ! As you pray in conclusion of this day's study, use your time of *Adoration* to exalt your Heavenly Father for providing a way to spend eternity in His presence. Humbly *Admit* those times when you lack faith due to not being able to physically see the Lord. In *Gratefulness*, remember and share with Him all you have been blessed with because of your personal relationship with Jesus. Conclude your time *Asking*, in expectation, for confirmation of your faith through understanding His words in 1 John.

A – "Eternal One, true Father of time past, present and future, how awesome and great You are to provide through Jesus a way for me to have eternal life!"

C- "I confess the times that my life shows I am lacking faith that You are present."

T – "Thank you Jesus for setting Your will aside on my behalf and saving me while I was yet a sinner."

S – "Help me to have an eternal perspective today as I walk through the hours of events and come in contact with the people You have placed in my life."

> *"The secret of my success? It is simple. It is found in the BIBLE,*
> *'In all thy ways acknowledge Him and He shall direct thy paths'"*
> ~ ***George Washington Carver*** ~

D A Y   T H R E E

ON MY KNEES:

Sometimes, just before the sun pokes above the horizon, there is a sweet quiet of gray skies. The new day hasn't really begun and it is good to settle into a slow start with just the Lord and His Word. Relish this time with the Friend of friends.

Pray. "Heavenly Father, I come to You through the grace provided by Your Son, Jesus. I want You to be the priority in my life today. Show me more of Yourself and how I can be a better disciple."

Write. Purposefully write 1 John 1:3 in the "Write!" section of your study.

Read. Keep your Bible open to 1 John, stand up and boldly read Chapter 1 out loud.

INVESTIGATIVE STUDY

Aerial View

Streetview

Under the Rug

Apply!

INVESTIGATIVE STUDY
STREETVIEW: CHAPTER 1

We are going to do one more exercise before moving down to the next level of detail. Much of 1 John corresponds to the book of John. It seems as though John expected his readers to have read his previous book so he uses shorter phrases, almost like short hand.

Sometimes it is helpful to look at other references to better understand Scripture. Below, you will see the chapter divided into phrases with passages that are similar or expanded on the topic. Find and read the passages, then summarize how they deepen your understanding of the 1 John phrase. We will do the first five verses of the chapter today and the second five verses tomorrow.

"From the beginning…" in Verse 1

John 1:1 _____

_____

John 17:5 _____

_____

Colossians 1:13-17 _____

_____

"What we heard, saw and touched/handled…" in Verse 1

John 1:14 _____

_____

Luke 24:39 _____

_____

Acts 4:10-13, 18-20 _____

_____

2 Peter 1:16 _____

_____

"The eternal life…" in Verse 2

John 10:28 _____

_____

John 17:3 _____

_____

1 John 5:13 _____

_____

"Fellowship with Him…" in Verse 3

1 Corinthians 1:10 _____

_____

Galatians 2:7-9 _____

_____

Philippians 2:1-2 _____

_____

"Joy may be full/complete…" in Verse 4

John 15:9-11 _____

_____

Philippians 2:2 _____

_____

"Darkness..." in Verse 5

John 1:1-9 _____

_____

John 3:19-21 _____

_____

Ephesians 5:6-10 _____

_____

Psalm 27:1 _____

_____

Proverbs 4:18-19 _____

_____

A.C.T.S. PRAYER TIME

Have you ever noticed that when there is sin in your life, it not only affects your relationship with your heavenly Father, but also your relationship with others? Faith in Christ ushers us into a new family, God's family. How we live our lives affects the whole family.

Close your time today in *Adoration* of our perfect heavenly Father. Next, take time to *Confess* as His child the many privileges that we so often take for granted. *Thank* Him for His daily cleansing and end with any *Supplication* you want to make in light of what you learned from your time with the Lord today.

A – "Father, I come to You today praising Your role in my life as the perfect Father. You always give me what is good."

C – "Lord, forgive me for taking for granted the unconditional love You give me daily because of Christ, My Savior."

T – "Thank you for forgiving me all of my sins and then giving me eternal life in Your Son."

S – "Lord, I need the "mind of Christ" to understand 1 John. Help me to not only understand, but let it change me from the inside out."

D A Y   F O U R

ON MY KNEES:

Cheer up! You are coming into the very presence of the One and Only Living God of the universe. Is it not unbelievable that He would be ready and waiting for us to come to Him? He does not force us to come. He does not demand us to sit. He beckons and waits on us. How incredible! Begin on your knees before continuing in His Word.

Pray. "Lord, I come into Your presence with thanksgiving. I come singing for joy in You, as my rock of salvation. Reveal more of Yourself to me and impress Your ways into my heart as I study Your Word. Help me to stay focused during our time together."

Write. Open your Scriptures to 1 John 1:4 and meditate on the verse as you write it out in your Sword Study pages.

Read. Read the first chapter of 1 John once again.

INVESTIGATIVE STUDY
STREETVIEW: CHAPTER 1

INVESTIGATIVE STUDY

1 Aerial View

2 Streetview chapter

3 Under the Rug

Apply!

Are you ready for a few more revelations about the background of John's phrases in 1 John? Once again, we will spend time looking at other passages in Scripture to better understand where John is coming from when he wrote this letter.

Some of the passages will be from John's pen, while some will be from other inspired Bible authors. Look up the passages listed under each phrase and note what you find that further describes the 1 John phrase.

Though the information God could have given us would overflow the earth (John 21:25), He gave us just 66 books in His Word. Each of these passages give you additional information. Be sure to glean as much as possible from each one and write down what you find.

"God is light…" in Verse 5

John 8:12* _____

_____

John 9:5 _____

_____

John 12:35-36 _____

_____

"He is in the light" in Verse 7

Proverbs 4:18 _____

_____

Matthew 5:14-16 _____

_____

1 Peter 2:9 _____

_____

"We make Him a liar..." in Verse 10

Numbers 23:19 _____

_____

Hebrews 6:16-18 _____

_____

Titus 1:1-3 _____

_____

A.C.T.S. PRAYER TIME

Joy! John desired that his letter would make our joy full, or complete. The good news of being able to have fellowship with the God of Creation and His Son for all eternity, and as a side bonus with one another, was to result in joy. How great to know that we do not have to go through life's lessons blindly or alone! Praise the Lord in your time of *Adoration* for His gift of fellowship, and *Confess* the times when human relationships overshadow the importance of your time with Jesus. *Thank* God for the honor of fellowshipping with Him and that He calls you friend. In *Supplication*, ask that you would desire time with Him above all things.

A – "Hallelujah! God of wonder, God of praise, what a joy it is that I am able to come into Your presence, and have a relationship with You, and that You desire to meet with me."

C – "Forgive me, Father, for the many times I take for granted my ability to come to You, for making You wait, for not holding our times together as my highest priority."

T – "Thank you, Lord, for allowing me into Your holy presence. Thank you for not ruling from afar, but instead, for loving me and communicating intimately with me through Your Word."

S – "Give me an inextinguishable desire to fellowship with You every day. I want to know You more!"

"This Book (the BIBLE) had to be written by one of three people: good men, bad men or God. It couldn't have been written by good men because they said it was inspired by the revelation of God. Good men don't lie and deceive. It couldn't have been written by bad men because bad men would not write something that would condemn themselves. It leaves only one conclusion. It was given by divine inspiration of God."
~ *John Wesley* ~

DIGGING DEEPER

Walking in the light or walking in the dark is the question of the day. Turn and read Galatians 5:19-25. In verses 19-21, using a red colored pencil, underline those things listed as "of the flesh" (darkness).

In verses 22-25, using a green colored pencil, underline those things listed as "fruit of the Spirit" (light).

Where do you find yourself walking?

D A Y   F I V E

ON MY KNEES:

We have come to the end of Week 2. Are you getting used to coming here every day? Do you feel settled in the pattern of fellowshipping with the Lord?

Pray. "Holy, Holy, Holy is Your Name! Father, I come in awe of Your invitation to fellowship in Your presence. Please help me to sit quietly in Your presence and listen to Your wisdom. I want to be an obedient child. I want to know more of You so that I might walk in the light for You."

Write. Verses 5 and 6 of 1 John, Chapter 1 contrast the light and dark. As you write, hear the Lord speak through His words. Meditate on these things.

Read. Slowly and purposefully read 1 John 1 so that the familiarity doesn't cause your mind to wander.

Apply!

INVESTIGATIVE STUDY
UNDER THE RUG: KEY WORDS

The UNDER THE RUG portion of the INVESTIGATIVE STUDY is one of the most exciting parts of your Sword Study. As we move down from a STREETVIEW to this level, it is as if you are moving from the top of the trees, to the root system. As we overturn the soil, just beneath the surface, we will see things that are not evident at a cursory glance. You will gain great understanding of God and His heart as you investigate the Word in this way.

UNDER THE RUG has two parts: Word Studies and Cross-references. During the Word Study process, we will determine Key Words in the chapter and then look at their Greek and/or corresponding Hebrew words and dictionary definitions for greater understanding. Our second step of the UNDER THE RUG level is Cross-referencing, which involves taking the Greek or Hebrew word and finding it in additional passages throughout the Bible. Today, we will describe the Word Study format and choose Key Words for 1 John, Chapter 1.

Word Study:

Below you will find an abbreviated overview of the three-part Word Study process; Word Studies will be a part of each chapter study. In preparation for next week, briefly review the Word Study process so you will be able to put it into practice as you go UNDER THE RUG.

In PART A: We will look up the Key Word we chose in the Strong's Concordance and discover its Strong's number, which will lead us to the Greek word representing our English word.

In PART B: We will look up the Strong's number in a Greek lexicon or dictionary to discover further explanations of the word's meaning in Greek. The resources for Part B in the Sword Studies are "The Complete Word Study Dictionary" by Spiro Zodhiates and "Vine's Concise Dictionary of the Bible" by W.E. Vine. You may want to further investigate by using other Bible dictionaries, software such as Logos or online resources such as www.GreatTreasures.org.

In PART C: We will choose the correct meaning for the use of the word in 1 John.

What is the Strong's Concordance?

The Strong's Concordance is a very useful tool for studying God's Word. It lists every word used in the King James Version Bible. You can look up a Bible passage, choose a Key Word and then look it up in the Strong's Concordance to see all the other verses that also include the same word.

Strong's is also helpful for locating Scripture verses which you remember partially but can't recall their book, chapter and/or verse. For example, you know there is a verse that says our hairs are numbered, but you aren't sure where it is in the Bible. You could look up the word "numbered" in a Strong's Concordance and it would give you a listing of all the verses that contain the word "numbered". You would then find Matthew 10:30 where God said that "the very hairs of your head are all numbered."

Each word also has a number next to it in the Strong's Concordance. The number represents a Hebrew or Greek word. In the back of the concordance Hebrew and Greek words are listed by number and explained by a short English definition. Strong's is useful even if you normally use other Bible versions, though you may need to use Bible Gateway or a KJV Bible to find the exact wording of the passage you are studying.

For your Word Studies, we will walk step-by-step through this process with two Key Words of Chapter 1 of 1 John. Choosing Key Words can be somewhat subjective, so you may choose different words than what we chose. After you learn the process, use the steps to do additional study on the words that we didn't include to deepen your knowledge of God's Word.

Using your Bible, let's look back over 1 John, Chapter One and mark Key Words. These are words that are repeated or seem to be key to what the author is trying to highlight to his readers and us. Be sure to mark all references to God, Jesus and the Holy Spirit. We have given you symbols to use for the Trinity and a few others below. Be creative with the way you mark other words that you feel are Key Words.

△ – God, the Father   ⟁ – God, the Son   ⋈ – God, the Spirit

☺ – Fellowship   ✷ – Light   ▭ – Sin

In the future, as you do the "Write" portion of the ON YOUR KNEES section, be sure to mark all references to God and any other words you consider to be Key Words.

Now, turn to your handwritten copy of 1 John. Mark the words above that you find in your first 6 verses. In the future, as you do the "Write" portion of the ON YOUR KNEES section, be sure to mark all references to God and any other words you consider to be Key Words. For example, as you were writing verses 5 and 6 today, when you came to the word "Him" in verse 5, you would have placed a triangle above or around the pronoun for God.

Next, notice the additional symbols in the left margin of your "Write!" page. The symbols for God, the Father, Son and Holy Spirit have been placed on each page. This area enables you to note, in 3 or 4 words, what you learn about the respective person of the Trinity. Go ahead and start at verse 1 of 1 John, looking for the symbols you have marked for the Trinity. Note what you learn about Him under each symbol for verses 1-6.

NOTE! *Do not interrupt your copying time to note what you learn about God in the margin, do that after you have finished copying.*

A.C.T.S. PRAYER TIME

Using the 1 John 1:5 and 6 verses that you wrote today, close your time in prayer to the God, Who is light and asks us to fellowship with Him in the light!

A – _____

C – _____

T – _____

S – _____

"Men do not reject the BIBLE because it contradicts itself but because it contradicts them."
~ E. Paul Hovey ~

Dwight L. Moody: Light to Chicago (continued)

(We now present the conclusion of a January 14, 1870, interview with the Reverend Dwight L. Moody with three junior reporters from the River Oaks News Club. Let's see if Alex Thomas, Zachary Baker and Hunter Nelson can learn more about the Christian life as they explore more about the Reverend D.L. Moody.)

Alex: You began your ministry with a mission Sunday School, and then it grew to become a church. Is that correct, Rev. Moody?

Moody: It is. But the story doesn't end there. The War Between the States lay ahead. And when the Union Army set up Camp Douglas outside Chicago, I realized that God had soldiers, too.

Zachary: What did you do?

Moody: We set up groups to minister to the fighting men. I traveled throughout the state and then the country to reach them for Christ.

Hunter: What do you mean by "reach"?

Moody: Another great question, my young friend. I showed the men how their sin—the wrongs they had done—separated them from God. Then I showed them how to repent and surrender to a full faith in Christ, who died on the cross to cleanse them from sin. I prayed with men from both sides, teaching and allowing the Holy Spirit to lead them to a knowledge of Him.

Alex: Now I understand! You used the war as an opportunity for evangelism.

Moody: Yes, indeed. God can use even sad times to draw people to Himself. The same thing happened with the fire.

Zachary: Oh! I know what you're talking about! The Great Chicago Fire, right?

Moody (*with sadness*): Yes. When the Fire came, our family lost almost everything—but, praise God, not what was most precious. My wife and three children were fine. But the loss of our church buildings made me realize I had made plans and then asked God to help me with them. From that point on, I surrendered to His desires. I would preach His Word to the world.

Hunter: Missions! That means you did missions, right?

Moody: Yes, my boy. My musician friend Ira Sankey and I, along with our wives, traveled to the United Kingdom, where we held many evangelistic crusades. God used us to help bring about revival in that part of the world. Thousands upon thousands came to each crusade, from England to Ireland to Scotland and back again. We were honored to serve as His messengers.

Alex: I have a quote from you during that time (reading): "I know perfectly well that, wherever I go and preach, there are many better preachers . . . than I am; all that I can say about it is that the Lord uses me."

Moody: Yes, that sounds like something I would have said, son. I can take no credit for the Lord's work.

Zach: And when you returned to the United States, you continued your crusades, right?

Moody: That's correct. We toured the East coast to share the gospel of Christ and also held a crusade in our beloved Chicago. It lasted for sixteen weeks, and as many as 10,000 people came to know the Lord.

Hunter: People came to know Christ back in the United States, too?

Moody (*chuckles*): Indeed they did, my boy. Indeed they did.

Alex: And there's more. Before long, you began a new ministry through Bible education, Reverend Moody. You opened the Northfield Seminary for Young Women and the Mount Hermon School for Boys in your home state of Massachusetts. Is that correct, sir?

Moody: It is. I consider these some of my most important avenues of kingdom work.

Zachary: But why schools, Rev. Moody?

Moody: I wanted to train young people to continue the work of reaching the inner city for Christ. Here, they could experience true fellowship as they prepared for Him to use them in great ways. We also began a summer conference ministry, for which we brought in some wonderful Bible teachers and preachers.

Hunter: So you were training average people to do great things?

Moody: Yes indeed. As I said at the time, "If this world is going to be reached, I am convinced that it must be done by men and women of average talent. After all, there are comparatively few people who have great talents." God can do wonderful work through hearts surrendered and trained to share His good news.

Alex: And that's just what you saw happen.

Moody: That's right. The gospel was shared at home and abroad. Our school at Mount Hermon, for example, helped birth what became known as the Student Volunteer Movement for Foreign Missions.

Zachary: I read about that! As the result of this movement, thousands of young people have begun volunteering to serve Christ overseas.

Moody: Yes. But I am growing old, and the work remains unfinished. I find myself asking the Father what else I can do, what further legacy I can leave. Not long ago, the Lord led me to open the Chicago Bible Institute, an even more extensive ministry training school than the two in Massachusetts.

Hunter: I know the Lord will guide you in His way.

Moody: To be sure, young man, to be sure.

Alex: Thank you for speaking with us today, Reverend Moody. We will pray with you about the future needs in Chicago and throughout the world. Thank you for all you've shared with us and with the many who have come to know Christ because of your faithfulness.

Moody: Long ago, I heard the British evangelist Henry Varley say, "It remains to be seen what the Lord can do with a man wholly consecrated to Christ." From then on, I determined to be such a man. And that is my prayer for you three as well.

Alex, Zachary and Hunter: Thank you, sir! God be with you, sir.

D A Y   O N E

ON MY KNEES:

Welcome to a brand new week and a deeper look at 1 John through Word Studies and Cross References. Before we dig in, let's go to the Lord in prayer. We are headed for a couple of days of very meaty meals from the Word, so let's bow before Him in preparation.

Pray. "Heavenly Father, as I start this new week, help me to understand that You are a holy God, righteous in all ways. Help me to have a heart and mind that is prepared to hear the meat of Your Word. Convict me, mold me and reveal to me the standards You desire for me as I walk through my days. In Jesus' name, amen. "

Write. Begin this week's writing by copying 1 John 1:7 in your "Write!" section.

Read. Start your week by re-reading the first chapter of 1 John.

INVESTIGATIVE STUDY
UNDER THE RUG:
WORD STUDY - "FELLOWSHIP"

INVESTIGATIVE STUDY

Aerial View

Streetview

Under the Rug

Apply!

In the first chapter of 1 John, some of the Key Words we considered were *light*, *message* and *joy*, but the words; *fellowship* and *sin* stood out among the others, so we will focus on these over the next several days. We will begin with *fellowship.*

Often we think of *fellowship* as an event at church with food, children bounding about and visiting with our friends. A variety of thoughts can come into our mind as we prepare to attend. "What will I wear? I wonder if 'so and so' will be there? I am not sure if I feel like being around people tonight." After we come home, we begin to evaluate. "What did she mean by that? I wonder if I answered that question right? Why did he ask that question?"

What is true, Biblical *fellowship*?

PART A: If you were to look up the word *fellowship* in Strong's Concordance, you would find that the Strong's number assigned to it is 2842. Note this, because we will use this number to look up detailed explanations of the original Greek word in Part B. Below is the transliteration, the pronunciation, and the basic definition from the Strong's lexicon:

2842. *Fellowship,* koinonia, *koy-nohn-ee'-ah;* from 2844; partnership, i.e. participation, communion.

117

PART B: Next, if you look up the number **2842** in another Greek lexicon, such as Vine's or Zodiates, you can discover more detailed explanations and uses of the word *fellowship* in Greek.

> ***Fellowship:***
>> 1) Communion, sharing in common
>> 2) From 2841, koinoneo; an associate, partaker, synonym to fellow traveler

PART C: Now that you have read through the definitions of *fellowship*, we will take a second look at how it is used in 1 John today. There are only a total of twelve uses of this word in the Bible, and four of them are here in 1 John. Tomorrow, we will investigate the other nine uses around the additional New Testament Scriptures.

1 John 1:3
To whom does *fellowship* apply, the first time the word is used in this verse? _____
_____

Who are the three entities *fellowshipping,* the second time the word is used? _____
_____

1 John 1:6
Who is supposed to be in *fellowship* according to this verse?_____
_____

When is *fellowship* broken with God? _____

1 John 1:7
Who is in *fellowship* in this verse? _____

　　　True *fellowship* is so refreshing! When we come together with like-minded believers and share all that God has recently done, is doing or looks like He is going to do, communion is so much more meaningful than any social event. Oh how blessed… how full of joy these times are to our spirit. Outfits, recipes, sports scores and conversations of weather suddenly lessen at a gathering of believers.

A . C . T . S .   P R A Y E R   T I M E

Open your Bible and turn to John 8:12*. What Jesus says about Himself is a perfect summary of 1 John 1:7, isn't it?

In *Adoration*, praise the Lord as the Light that keeps you from living in spiritual darkness. Take time to *Confess* and ask forgiveness for the times you chose not to walk in the light of His Word. *Thank* the Lord for His cleansing that brightens your world. During *Supplication*, ask that the Lord be the Light that you follow each day so you will draw closer to Him.

A –"Lord, You are the Light of the world and in You alone there is no darkness."

C –"Lord, forgive me for making the wrong choice today that resulted in my walking in darkness."

T –"Thank You, Lord for taking me out of the darkness of unbelief and giving me Your Holy Spirit as a guide in paths of righteousness."

S –"Lord, I want to follow You so that I can avoid the darkness that sin brings into my life. Help me to stand strong among my friends. I want to maintain my fellowship with You and encourage them to walk in Your ways at the same time."

"How can we be strangers, if we both follow Christ?"
~ Anonymous ~

D A Y   T W O

ON MY KNEES:

Getting to know Him through His Word takes the commitment of meeting Him each day. Keep up the great dedication!

Pray. "Lord, help me be willing to erase the list I have made for myself today. Help me to be eternally focused. Confirm the things I have planned for my day. I want to walk in Your light, fellowship with You and Your people. Show me what this means in Your Word today. Amen."

Write. Copy 1 John 1:8 onto the next lines of your "My Copy of 1 John" pages.

Read. Slowly and deliberately read 1 John 1 again.

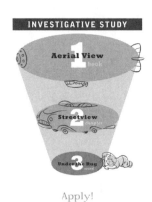

Apply!

INVESTIGATIVE STUDY
UNDER THE RUG:
CROSS REFERENCES - "FELLOWSHIP"

Oh, how uncomfortable and unsettling it is when fellowship is broken with a friend! As you go through the day, just about everything reminds you of the person. When there is trouble in a relationship, things need to be addressed in order to restore peace, fellowship and continue moving forward. Let's look at *fellowship* around the Word and see what we have to learn about our relationship with Christ, His people and the world.

Read Acts 2:41-47, then answer the questions below:

Who was *fellowshipping* in this passage? _____

What did they do together? _____
_____

Read 2 Corinthians 6:14, then answer the questions below:

What do we learn about *fellowship*? _____

What doesn't mix? _____

Read 2 Corinthians 13:11-14, then answer the questions below:

Who is at the heart of *fellowship* between the Christians according to this passage? _____
_____

What are Paul's exhortations to the believers? (List all) _____
_____

Read Philippians 2:1-2, then answer the questions below:

Among whom is the *fellowship* in this passage? _____

What are the results of the *fellowship*? _____
_____

What is included in the outcome of joy? _____

 Read Leviticus 26:11-12, and answer the questions below:

What is described in this passage? _____

Why would the Jewish people have related so well to the idea of *fellowship*? _____
_____

What fellowship does John 1:14 proclaim? _____
_____
_____
_____
_____

In light of all you have seen regarding *fellowship*, paraphrase 1 John 1:3 on the lines below: _____
_____
_____
_____
_____

APPLY!

As we looked at a few passages regarding joy and fellowship today, did your mind wander to those in your church, school or other spheres of life that give you joy when you fellowship with them? Spending time with a friend who is like-minded gives us reason to rejoice. List a few of your closest friends below. Give one or two of them a call or e-mail to arrange for a time to get together this week. Plan to share what God is doing in your life and listen to the work He is doing in theirs! Take this opportunity to also consider if there is anyone with whom you need to restore fellowship.

_____   _____

_____   _____

_____   _____

A . C . T . S .   P R A Y E R   T I M E

Before ending in prayer today, read Romans 7:18. Is that your battle today? Sin is always going to be an ongoing battle, but be encouraged!   God has a way out for all those that are in Christ. *Praise* God for sending His Son to rescue you from sin's power in your life. *Confess* that the "wishing" to do good is what you desire, but the doing of good often fails each day. *Thank* Him for sending His Spirit to give You His power. In your time of *Supplication*, ask for His power to replace sin's power in your life in your areas of temptation.

A - "Lord, You are the Way, the Truth and the Life. Your truth guides me in a world that says there is no absolute truth."

C - "Lord, I am sorry that I can be so easily deceived about my sin by thinking I have a right to respond in anger."

T - "Thank You for Your Word that teaches me truth that I can live by each day."

S - "Lord, when I do sin, as Your Word says I will, I want to be quick to confess and get right with You."

Has it ever occurred to you that one hundred pianos all tuned to the same fork are automatically tuned to each other? They are of one accord by being tuned, not to each other, but to another standard to which each one must individually bow. So one hundred worshipers [meeting] together, each one looking away to Christ, are in heart nearer to each other than they could possibly be, were they to become 'unity' conscious and turn their eyes away from God to strive for closer fellowship."
~ *A. W. Tozer* ~

DIGGING DEEPER

The Bible gives us examples of walking in the light. Galatians 5:22-26 shows us the fruits of the Spirit. When we walk in these ways, we are walking in the light. Look up the passage and list the qualities that will characterize our life as a result of walking in the Spirit.

_____

_____

_____

_____

_____

_____

_____

_____

_____

_____

DAY THREE

ON MY KNEES:

Checkmark, checkmark, checkmark. Do you make daily lists and then put check marks or lines through each activity or chore as they are completed? Do you add to your list if you do something that wasn't originally on the list? We often feel so good when we accomplish our lists that we get the same attitude about our time with the Lord. Pray, check. Write, check. Fill in the blanks, check. On with the day... Oh, that we would stop and hear from Him so that our lists would be adjusted to where He leads. Let's ask for that before we go on.

Pray. "Heavenly Father, my time with You is the most important part of my day. Teach me to put Your agenda over my own. I really don't want to view our time as an item on my list. Help me see Your plans and ways for my days. Give me a heart of dedication to You. I know that my plans will not succeed unless they come from You. I want to trust You with my days. Amen."

Write. 1 John 1:9 is a powerful verse. Copy it on your pages in a unique way, perhaps in cursive or in a different color.

Read. Re-read Chapter 1 of 1 John.

INVESTIGATIVE STUDY

Apply!

INVESTIGATIVE STUDY
UNDER THE RUG:
WORD STUDY - "SIN"

S-I-N. We don't hear this word often in everyday conversation. We **may** hear it in our homes or churches, but infrequently in the grocery store, mall or at group events. Even less frequently do we hear it spoken of or discussed in movies, TV shows or radio programs. This is an interesting fact to consider. We see *sin* escalating in all of these areas, yet calling *sin* a *sin* has dramatically decreased. Interesting.

After looking at the comparison between light and dark, darkness can be described as the presence of *sin* and light as the absence of *sin*. If this is true, and we are to walk in the light, we had better make sure we truly know what the Bible means when it uses the word *sin*. We had best not rely on our own paraphrased definitions. Therefore, let's go to the Greek word(s) used in 1 John for a clear understanding of the word that has the power to break our daily fellowship with God, the potential to cause us to be absent of truth and, most detrimentally, the potential consequence of eternal death for us!

Word Study of Sin:

PART A: If you were to look up the word *sin* in Strong's Concordance, you would find that the Strong's numbers assigned to it are 264 and 266. Note this, because we will use these numbers to look up detailed explanations of the original Greek words in Part B. Below are the transliterations, the pronunciations, and the basic definitions from the Strong's lexicon:

> **264. *Sin.*** <u>hamartano</u>, *Ham-ar-tan'-o,* verb; to miss the mark (and so as not share in the prize), to err, offend, sin, trespass.

> **266. *Sin.*** <u>hamartia</u>, *ham-ar-tee'-ah,* noun from 264: offense, sin(-ful).

PART B: Next, if you look up the numbers **264** and **266** in another Greek lexicon, such as Vine's or Zodiates, you can discover more detailed explanations and uses of the word *sin* in Greek.

> **264. *Sin*,** verb; to err in action, in respect to a prescribed law, i.e., to commit errors, to do wrong.

> > 1) Sinning against God

> > > A) Act of sin, 1 John 1:10, 2:1

> > > B) Present tense indicates, not the committal of an act, but the continuous practice of "sin", 1 John 3:6 (twice), 1 John 3:8, 9.

> > > C) Present tense indicates the condition resulting from an act, such as "unto death", 1 John 5:16

> > 2) Sinning against Christ
> > 3) Sinning against Man
> > 4) Sinning against Jewish Law
> > 5) Sinning against oneself
> > 6) Sinning against earthly masters

> **266. *Sin*,** noun; an offense in relation to God with emphasis on guilt.

> > 1) Aberration (wandering) from the truth, error
> > 2) Aberration, (wandering) from a prescribed law or rule of duty, whether in general or of particular sins.
> > 3) The consequences of sin, the guilt and punishment of sin, willful and intentional sin. (1 John 5:16)

PART C: Stop. Pray for quiet. The definitions that you just studied are absolutely key to un-

125

derstanding the distinction between a believer who commits individual *sin*, and an unbeliever who practices *sin* as they walk in the darkness. John describes this perfectly and clearly in 1 John 3:8-10. Read this passage now.

Now that you have the definitions of the various forms of the word *sin*, let's look at the verses in 1 John that use the word *sin*. Circle "noun" or "verb" next to the verse reference and write in any notes to yourself that your understanding of the definition brings to light.

1 John 1:7   Noun or Verb   Note to Self about sin: _____

1 John 1:8   Noun or Verb   Note to Self about sin: _____

1 John 1:9   Noun or Verb   Note to Self about sin: _____

1 John 1:9   Noun or Verb   Note to Self about sin: _____

1 John 2:1   Noun or Verb   Note to Self about sin: _____

1 John 2:1   Noun or Verb   Note to Self about sin: _____

1 John 2:2   Noun or Verb   Note to Self about sin: _____

1 John 2:12   Noun or Verb   Note to Self about sin: _____

1 John 3:4   Noun or Verb   Note to Self about sin: _____

1 John 3:4   Noun or Verb   Note to Self about sin: _____

1 John 3:5   Noun or Verb   Note to Self about sin: _____

1 John 3:5   Noun or Verb   Note to Self about sin: _____

1 John 3:6   Noun or Verb   Note to Self about sin: _____

1 John 3:8   Noun or Verb   Note to Self about sin: _____

1 John 3:8   Noun or Verb   Note to Self about sin: _____

1 John 3:9   Noun or Verb   Note to Self about sin: _____

1 John 3:9   Noun or Verb   Note to Self about sin: _____

1 John 4:10	Noun or Verb	Note to Self about sin: _____
1 John 5:16	Noun or Verb	Note to Self about sin: _____
1 John 5:16	Noun or Verb	Note to Self about sin: _____
1 John 5:16	Noun or Verb	Note to Self about sin: _____
1 John 5:17	Noun or Verb	Note to Self about sin: _____
1 John 5:17	Noun or Verb	Note to Self about sin: _____
1 John 5:18	Noun or Verb	Note to Self about sin: _____

Now, go back and look at all of the verses that you marked as having *sin* in the verb form. Determine if the person is committing an individual *sin*, or practicing *sin* as a lifestyle. Mark each in a different way to remind yourself of the two different individuals. (Hint: It is always helpful to note about whom John is speaking.)

A.C.T.S. PRAYER TIME

Cleanse me with hyssop, and I will be clean; wash me,
and I will be whiter than snow. Let me hear joy and gladness;
let the bones you have crushed rejoice.
Hide your face from my sins and blot out all my iniquity.
~ Psalm 51:7-9 ~

Using Psalm 51:7-9, write a sentence for each attribute of the A.C.T.S. Prayer model to prepare yourself for your closing prayer time.

A - *Adoration* _____

C - *Confession* _____

T - *Thanksgiving* _____

S - *Supplication* _____

DAY FOUR

ON MY KNEES:

Looking back over the last ten days, it is truly amazing to realize that we have learned so much from studying only ten verses. This is such a good reminder that the Word is infinitely deep. Each time we come to His feet in expectation of drawing near, He promises to draw nearer. Our hearts should rejoice in His favor and bow in humble reverence.

Pray. "Lord, I am getting used to meeting with You each day. Help this to never grow old or be viewed as a task in my mind. I want to desire to make our time a non-optional part of my days. I see more and more each day how walking in Your light makes my burdens and outlook better. Teach me more of Your ways today. In Jesus' name, I pray. Amen."

Write. You have one last verse to write and you will have completed the first chapter of 1 John! Go ahead and copy the tenth verse in your copy of 1 John.

Read. Now, read your own handwritten copy of 1 John 1 before beginning the INVESTIGATIVE STUDY portion of your Sword Study.

Apply!

INVESTIGATIVE STUDY
UNDER THE RUG:
CROSS REFERENCES - "SIN"

"For to a person who is good in His sight He has given wisdom and knowledge and joy, while to the sinner He has given the task of gathering and collecting so that he may give to one who is good in God's sight. This too is vanity and striving after wind."
~ Ecclesiastes 2:26 ~

Understanding the definitions of *sin* can be oppressive if we ourselves have not been forgiven of <u>our</u> *sins*. Do you see that this is not missing a target in a game; this is losing fellowship, and/or potentially losing the ultimate, eternal game. *Sin* that is not forgiven through belief and trust in Jesus as the Savior is *sin* without the "guilty" verdict removed.

We must understand the rules of fellowship.

From our research of the definition of fellowship on Day One, the core ingredient is "common ground." We must understand that we cannot have fellowship with God without having a **relationship** with Jesus.

God is Light and He does not fellowship in the darkness. It is only through His Son, Jesus, that He can have a relationship with us and see us without sin. As a result of the event we call "salvation,"

He looks at us, sees us wrapped in Jesus' righteousness, and accepts us as His adopted children; otherwise, He sees us wrapped in our sin and, as a perfect God, cannot enter into a relationship with us. If we have trusted Jesus as our payment for sin, we have the seed of Christ, the Holy Spirit, dwelling in us. Then, we have not only been saved from the penalty of sin, which is death, but have victorious power over sin's bondage and are able to walk in the Light.

While the next exercise may be repetitive for the Believer, it is essential as a foundation for us to look at the cross references for *sin*. We will return to the cross references that refer to *sin* in relationship to fellowship in a moment. First, let's make certain that we have a relationship with God.

According to Romans 3:23, who has *sinned*? _____

According to Romans 6:23, what is the penalty of *sin*? _____

According to 1 Peter 2:24-25, who died for our *sins*? _____

According to Romans 10:9-10, what must we do to be saved? _____
_____

According to Hebrews 10:26-27, what happens to the person who rejects the message of salvation?
_____

Read Psalm 14:2-3 and answer the following two questions:

What was God searching for in verse 2? _____

According to verse 3, who does good? _____

Read Job 15:14-16* and answer the following two questions:

How does God view the person who continues in *sin*? _____

Is man born righteous? _____

Now, we can return to John's focus on fellowship in the light of understanding that he was speaking to the believer in 1 John 1's reference to fellowship and *sin*.

What is removed when I repent, according to Psalm 32:5? _____

Read Proverbs 28:13.

What is the result of trying to hide *sin*? _____

What is the result of confessing my *sin*? _____

What hint does Ephesians 4:26 give us to help keep our fellowship unbroken between men and God?
_____

According to 1 Timothy 5:20, how can church leaders help keep their body of Christ walking in the light? _____

When Jesus was treated unjustly, what example does He give us in 1 Peter 2:20-23? _____
_____

When we walk in the light, we enjoy unbroken fellowship with the Lord and His people. We experience joy, show evidence of Christ as Lord of our life, and confirm our authentic Christianity.

Where are you in the "game?" Have you trusted that Jesus died on the cross in your place? He paid your penalty for *sin*. Do you know if you are His child? Salvation is a specific time and place. It is hitting the mark.

Sanctification is continuing to practice walking like Jesus, knowing that we are already His – just needing to become more like Him as a family member. He is discipling us through His Word!

A . C . T . S .   P R A Y E R   T I M E

1 John tells us that as believers we can still *sin*, but we have an Advocate, someone who will tell the Father we are forgiven… His name is Jesus! Praise Jesus for His sacrificial death in your place. Confess those times you don't take *sin* seriously enough. Thank Jesus for His willingness to go to the Cross to pay *sin's* penalty. Ask God in your time of Supplication to live each day for the one who died in your place.

A - "Lord, I praise Your Holy name."

C - "Lord, often I find my mind wandering to all that I need to accomplish today. I hate feeling like I am just going through the motions."

T - "Thank You for the grace and lovingkindness You show to me even when I haven't done my best for You."

S - "Lord, I want to experience the abundant life in Christ as I study 1 John."

"I have great assurance when I study my own conversion, when I discuss it with other men, when I look over the 25 years of my pilgrimage with Christ; I have great assurance of having come to know Him. But even now, if I were to depart from the faith and walk away and keep going in that direction into heresy and worldliness, it could be the greatest of proofs that I never knew Him, that the whole thing was a work of the flesh."

~ Paul Washer ~

D A Y   F I V E

ON MY KNEES:

Today brings us to a very special activity in our Sword Study. We have been waiting for you to arrive here! Begin in prayer first.

Pray. "Lord, You are my God. When we looked at Leviticus, I was reminded of how the Israelites grumbled and complained even though You had provided so much for them. Yet, You came to them again and again, offering Your fellowship nevertheless. I admit that I find myself grumbling about my life sometimes, too. I want to dwell in Your presence and fellowship in joy. Thank You for reminding me of Your goodness in Your Word."

Write. Make sure that you have marked all references to God in your "My Copy of 1 John".

Read. Read all five chapters of 1 John today before heading to do your Day 10 Diagram.

Apply!

INVESTIGATIVE STUDY
1-2-3 SUMMARIZE: CHAPTER 1

Congratulations! You have finished the INVESTIGATIVE STUDY of the first chapter of 1 John. We have a neat way for you to wrap up all that you have been learning over the last two weeks.

As you turn the page, you will see a "Day 10 Diagram." Around the edges of the picture, there are blanks for you to fill out. In the center, the Day 10 Diagram will have a picture that summarizes the chapter. If you have any problems figuring out how to fill in your Day 10 Diagram, talk to a parent; the Parent Guidebook includes the answer key to this diagram.

☐ To begin, look at the top of the Day 10 Diagram. Fill in the chapter number. Look at Week 1, Day 5 for the original title you created for 1 John 1. Review what you wrote and refine your title with the new insights that you have learned over the last 10 days.

☐ Next, which verse from the chapter do you think was the "key verse?"

☐ On the right of the page, transfer your key Greek words from this chapter. Write the English words on the top line after the words "Greek Words." Transfer the Greek spellings and write a short definition of their meanings.

☐ On the bottom of the Diagram page, transfer the most important things that you learned about God through marking the references about Him on your "Write!" pages.

You've observed how strongly John emphasizes the difference between light and darkness, so you won't be surprised to see two contrasting areas in this summary drawing of 1 John 1. As you study the diagram, look for the beloved disciple John standing near a map of Asia. On the blank above John's head, write the name of the city from which he wrote the letter of 1 John. Then, on the lines to the right of John, note four things that you learned about him through your studies these past two weeks.

Thunder clouds of false teaching were looming over the people of Asia in John's day. On the line in the stormy sky, write the name of the untrue belief system from which John wished to protect the believers. Though the dark clouds seem huge and threatening, God has provided a path into His light by way of the cross of Christ. What did we learn was nailed to the cross so that we could live forever with God? Fill in the note on the cross and thank God once again for his amazing gift of grace! Write the Greek words for *sin* on each side of the middle beam of the cross.

Now, on the open Bible at the top of the cross, write the name that John called Jesus in verse 1:1.

Our fellow believers in the diagram have crossed from the darkness into the light of eternal life with Christ through the cross. Write the Greek word for "fellow travelers" above the heads of Sword Study travelers. Mark the lighthouse on the mountainside with one characteristic that John says in Chapter 1 that God is, and two characteristics that God is not.

Remember that John also said that he was proclaiming a joyful message about the new fellowship that is possible for those who have put their faith in Christ? Just like the recipients of John's letter, our belief in Christ's finished work of the cross makes it possible for us to enjoy an ongoing love relationship with others. Under the lighthouse, write the word, "Fellowship," and then list those with whom John says we can now have fellowship. You can enjoy that fellowship this week as you meet with the Lord each day, and as you gather with your family and friends who also know Jesus.

Now that you have completed your Diagram, take a few moments to consider the full picture. Be sure to share your thoughts with your family during the Family Bonfire time this week.

Greek Words:

Chapter:

Title:
Key Verse:

133

A.C.T.S. PRAYER TIME

"The LORD is good unto them that wait for him, to the soul that seeketh him."
~ Lamentations 3:25 KJV ~

A - Adoration_____

C - Confession_____

T - Thanksgiving_____

S - Supplication_____

DIGGING DEEPER

During the Key Word process, it was difficult to choose between words this week. There was a struggle between the words *fellowship* and *light*. If you have additional time this weekend, working through the Word Study below on *light* would be well worth your efforts!

PART A: If you were to look up the word *light* in Strong's Concordance, you would find that the Strong's number assigned to it in 1 John is 5457. We will use this number to look up the detailed explanation of the Greek word in Part B. Below are the transliteration (the way the word is written in English), the pronunciation, and the basic definition from the Strong's lexicon (dictionary).

5457. *Light.* phōs. *foce,* from obs. phaō (to shine, or make manifest, espec. by rays; comp. 5316, 5346); luminousness (in the widest application, nat. or artif., abstr. or concr., lit. or fig.): - fire, light.

PART B: If you look up the number **5457** in another Greek lexicon, you can discover further explanations of the meaning of *light* in Greek.

PART C: Look at how light is used in these verses in 1 John:

1 John 1:5 _____
_____

1 John 1:7 _____
_____

1 John 2:8 _____
_____

1 John 2:9 _____

_____

1 John 2:10 _____

_____

Cross references of *light*

Job 33:29-31 _____

_____

Psalm 27:1 _____

_____

Isaiah 2:5 _____

_____

John 3:19 _____

_____

John 8:12_____

_____

John 12:36 _____

_____

2 Corinthians 6:14_____

_____

1 Peter 2:9 _____

_____

Do you have a favorite verse or two that have the word *light* in them? Take the time to go on your own rabbit trail of discovery. See how your additional knowledge adds to your understanding or changes it altogether. Allow the Holy Spirit to continue your lesson.

Nehemiah 9:19 _____

_____

1 Thessalonians 5:5 _____

_____

Colossians 1:12 _____

_____

Samuel Morris: Light Out of the Jungle
(Speech given at Taylor University Convocation,
September 9, 1892)

As I look out upon you, I see before me my fellow students as well as professors, staff and benefactors of Taylor University. But today, I call you my friends. And since you are my friends, I will share something most dear and precious: the story of the Lord God Almighty's great working in my life.

Like most of you, I did not begin my life in a university setting. But unlike most of you, I did not start out in this beautiful country, or even one you would consider civilized. My life began far from our fair city of Fort Wayne, Indiana.

Instead, it began in the heart of the jungle on the dark continent of Africa. I was born Prince Kaboo, son of a chieftain in the country you know as Liberia. There, I lived a simple life, a good life of family, hunting and tribal celebrations. A good life, that is, until war overtook our land and our people.

The debts of war mounted. One day, an enemy chief came to my father and demanded payback. "If you want peace, you must pay," he thundered.

"We will pay. We will pay!" my father pleaded.

"Yes, you will. You will pay with your son." Our opponent's words split the air—and my heart. Rough arms grabbed me from behind. Suddenly, I was a hostage, bound to the enemy until our tribe could pay its debts.

My father delivered gift after gift to the enemy chief. None brought satisfaction. "No," the wicked leader roared. "It will take more than that to pay what you owe."

Every day, he whipped me with a thorny, poisonous vine. Its venom soon infected the welts on my back, and I grew weak and sick. What would become of me?

I overheard my captors: "We're tired of waiting. His father had better bring enough goods this time, or we'll bury him alive." I could no longer stand, so they tied me to a wooden cross and prepared to beat me one last time.

I couldn't respond. I didn't care. All I wanted was relief from this unbearable pain—even if it meant death. As I hung over the grave they had prepared for me, I could feel my life slipping away.

Suddenly, a bright light shone all around me. The knots untwisted. The ropes fell off my hands and feet. Then I heard it: "Kaboo!"

Weak as I was, the voice pierced my heart. "RUN!"

The weakness dropped away as fast as the ropes had. Strength filled my body. I could stand. I could run! I bounded into the jungle as fast as I could, hiding in a hollow tree until darkness fell.

As I waited in the tree, I pondered the day's events. Who had spoken to me? What was the light? And what was happening to me now?

I had no answers, but I knew the voice spoke truth. I must leave, and quickly. If I returned home to my tribe, the enemy would kill not just me, but all my people.

Once darkness blanketed the jungle, I climbed out of the tree and again stood amazed. The bright light that led me to the tree shone once more. It lit the path before me, guiding me through the night and toward safety.

After many days of walking, I reached a coffee plantation. "Welcome," said a worker, offering to take me to his boss. They needed more laborers. Before I knew it, I had a job and brand-new clothes.

Soon, I noticed something different about the young man who had found me. I often found him kneeling on the floor. "What are you doing?" I asked.

"Praying to God, my Father in heaven," he answered. "Would you like to come with me to church? There, you can learn more about Him."

As I attended the church, I recognized God's presence. A missionary and graduate of Fort Wayne University (now Taylor) spoke on the conversion of the Apostle Paul. In his story, I recognized my own.

Everything began to fit together in my head and heart. God was the bright light. God had brought me out of captivity, out of the jungle and into my new home. And now, God would be my Master, the ruler and guide of my life.

That day, I repented of my sin and received Christ as my Savior and Lord. In obedience to the Bible, God's holy Book, I was baptized. An American missionary gave me the name of his sponsor, Samuel Morris. I was no longer Kaboo. The old things had passed away. Everything had become new.

But somehow, I couldn't help but wonder: Where would God take me next?

Read the conclusion of Samuel Morris' exciting speech next week!

DAY ONE

ON MY KNEES:

Righteousness and justice are the foundation of the Lord's throne; mercy and truth go before Him. We are a blessed people who know this to be true because we can walk in the light of His countenance! Come let us rejoice all day long in His name and exalt in His righteousness!

Pray. "Lord, as I hear those paraphrased words of Psalm 89:14-16, fill my heart with Your joy. Help me to understand all that I study today so that I might rejoice in Your Name all day long. Holy Spirit, remind me of Your words throughout this day, that I might walk in righteousness, faithfully."

Write. Please turn to your copy of 1 John and write out 1 John 2:1-3. Prayerfully review the words as you write them, soaking in their meaning.

Read. Begin this week by reading Chapters 1 and 2 of 1 John.

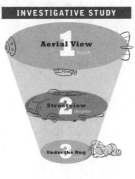

Apply!

INVESTIGATIVE STUDY
STREETVIEW: CHAPTER 2

As we studied the first chapter of 1 John, we heard John impress on us the importance of knowing that Jesus was God's Son and that He came to give us fellowship with the Father and Himself, as well as other like-minded believers.

Our focus will now turn to the second chapter of 1 John. Repeatedly, John tells us why he is writing this short letter in the next 29 verses. Be sure to watch for the "why's" and "who's" in this chapter as you read over it daily.

We will begin dissecting the chapter by taking each verse and writing a short, summary phrase in our own words. Try to use fewer than ten words for your summary phrase, just enough to remind yourself of what you thought the verse was saying. Do not turn this into a lengthy assignment. Remember, we are at the STREETVIEW level and our objective is to get an overview of the chapter before studying specific key words or themes. We will do the first half of the chapter today and the second half tomorrow.

Follow our lead; we have done the first two as examples for you.

Verse 1: <u>Don't sin, but if you do, Jesus is your Advocate.</u>

Verse 2: <u>Jesus is everyone's propitiation for sins.</u>

Verse 3: _____

Verse 4: _____

Verse 5: _____

Verse 6: _____

Verse 7: _____

Verse 8: _____

Verse 9: _____

Verse 10: _____

Verse 11: _____

Verse 12: _____

Verse 13: _____

Verse 14: _____

Verse 15: _____

A.C.T.S. PRAYER TIME

In 1 Timothy 1:17, Paul closes his letter to Timothy proclaiming God's characteristics as the King, who is eternal, immortal, invisible and the only God to give honor and glory. Close your time of study and fellowship with the Lord in prayer using Paul's character attributes as a launching pad of ***Adoration, Confession, Thanksgiving*** and ***Supplication*** to your God and King.

A - *Adoration* _____

C - *Confession* _____

T - *Thanksgiving* _____

S - *Supplication* _____

"The word of God hidden in the heart is a stubborn voice to suppress."
~ Billy Graham ~

DIGGING DEEPER

Do you ***know*** Him? What are His commandments? The Ten Commandments illustrate what a righteous walk of knowing God deeply and abiding with Him would look like, as they reflect His righteous character. Without looking them up in Exodus 20, write as many of the Ten Commandments as you can from memory on the lines below…

1. _____

2. _____

3. _____

4. _____

5. _____

6. _____

7. _____

8. _____

9. _____

10. _____

Ok, now you can look. Write in those you couldn't remember in a different colored pen or pencil.

DAY TWO

ON MY KNEES:

Where are you today? Are you in your normal, secluded spot with the Lord, or are you away from home? Regardless, go before the Lord in prayer asking for a protected time of fellowship with Him without any interruptions.

Pray. "God and Father, I come before you now in humble adoration, knowing that You alone are able to protect me, guide me and love me perfectly. I want to learn more of You and Your ways so that I might love You more and live in a way that is pleasing to You. I need Your strength even to desire Your ways. Thank You for revealing Yourself to me."

Write. As you write 1 John 2:4-6 in "My Copy of 1 John," feel free to highlight and mark words as you complete each writing assignment. This is a helpful way to cement the words in your mind.

Read. Conscientiously read 1 John, Chapter 2.

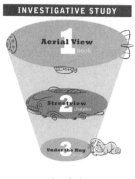

Apply!

INVESTIGATIVE STUDY
STREETVIEW: CHAPTER 2

Welcome back! We are on the last half of your Chapter 2 summary sentences. Be creative in your summaries so that as you look back on your notes, you will be able to remember the gist of what each verse said.

Verse 16: _____

Verse 17: _____

Verse 18: _____

Verse 19: _____

Verse 20: _____

Verse 21: _____

Verse 22: _____

Verse 23: _____

Verse 24: _____

Verse 25: _____

Verse 26: _____

Verse 27: _____

Verse 28: _____

Verse 29: _____

APPLY!

Go out in your neighborhood or to a local park and plan to walk one mile. As you walk, read through the Bible Memory Passage cards that correspond with your Sword Study. This walk will be one similar to what Jesus may have done as He walked with the disciples…speaking the words of His Father. Remember, we are to walk as He did!

A.C.T.S. PRAYER TIME

Going forward, we would like you to fill in your own "mini" prayer journal in the A.C.T.S. letters below. Try to personalize your prayers with what God has spoken to you during your study. Occasionally, as you look back over your prayers, you will be encouraged as you see how God has answered your supplications and matured your faith.

A - *Adoration* _____

C - *Confession* _____

T - *Thanksgiving* _____

S - *Supplication* _____

"The BIBLE fits man for life and prepares him for death"
~ Daniel Webster ~

DAY THREE

ON MY KNEES:

What freedom we have been given to enter without restraint into the company of the Holy God of the world…of the universe! Let us go to Him now in prayer before digging into His Word.

Pray. "Lord, calm my thoughts and slow my spirit as I join You in my study today. I want to stay focused on You, so please help keep my thoughts from wandering aimlessly. Also, Lord, I pray for my fellow friends in Christ around the world today that they would be encouraged in their study as well. There are times that I feel alone and different from my friends who aren't walking with You. I am so thankful to know that I am a part of Your bigger family."

Write. Next, write 1 John 2:7-9 in your "Write!" section.

Read. Please read Chapter 2 of 1 John.

INVESTIGATIVE STUDY

Apply!

INVESTIGATIVE STUDY
STREETVIEW: CHAPTER 2

After reading Chapter 2 three times this week, have you noticed how many times John repeated the phrases, "I write" and "I have written"? The repetition confirms the importance of what he wants to emphasize.

Today, we are going to fill in a graph of each time he uses the word "write" or any derivative of "write." We will also note the recipient, his reason for writing, and what he told them.

Verse	Verb Tense	To Whom	What	Why
1	I write, Present Tense	My Little/Dear Children	These Things	*So they won't sin *If they sin, they know they have an Advocate
7				
8				
12				
13				

Verse	Verb Tense	To Whom	What	Why
13				
13 (NIV 14)				
14				
14				
21		(See Verse 18 for hint!)		
26				

Now that you have completed the chart, did you notice how often John repeats himself? He addresses the "children", "fathers" and "young men" in verses 12 through 14 twice; first in the present tense and then in the past. Quickly, list on the lines below the recipients John addresses in this chapter:

_____

_____

_____

_____

Each of the titles John uses portrays a fatherly term of endearment. There is no doubt that the once "Son of Thunder" has softened a bit and is displaying fatherly love to his children in the faith. Beloved of Christ, may you hear the same love across the ages through his words from Jesus, the Lord and Savior.

APPLY!

On the lines below list reasons why we write to others,

✎ _____

✎ _____

✎ _____

✎ _____

Now, take the time to write a note to four different people for each of the reasons you listed above. Be sure to include God's words in your notes as they are the best, regardless of our reasons for writing, since they are good for all seasons!

A.C.T.S. PRAYER TIME

"Before the mountains were brought forth, Or ever You had formed the earth and the world, Even from everlasting to everlasting, You are God."
~ Psalm 90:2 NKJV ~

A - *Adoration* _____

C - *Confession* _____

T - *Thanksgiving* _____

S - *Supplication* _____

DIGGING DEEPER

Families are so special! On a separate piece of paper, create a Family Tree. Be creative! You could use actual photos to place next to your family members' names or make your tree on a poster board. Interview a grandparent and put a short paragraph of a special story next to each person's name.

D A Y   F O U R

ON MY KNEES:

Whoa! Are you in a hurry? Do you feel the need to rush off to events? Do you feel you must go a bit faster through your time with the Lord today because you have so much to do? Purposefully calm down, take a few deep breaths to lower your heart rate and begin your time in prayer. Share your heart with Him.

Pray. "Lord, I feel pressured to hurry. I don't want to short-change our time together. I know that You are able to redeem the time. I want to make our time a priority. Help me resist being anxious, and if I need to cut something out of the day so that we have more time together, show me what it is."

Write. Open your Bible to 1 John 2:10-13 to write the verses in the "Write!" section of your Sword Study.

Read. Please read 1 John 2 before you begin your study time.

INVESTIGATIVE STUDY

Aerial View
1

Streetview
2

Under the Rug
3

Apply!

INVESTIGATIVE STUDY
STREETVIEW: CHAPTER 2

As we enter the fourth day of investigating 1 John 2, we will be doing a treasure hunt of sorts. Hidden in this chapter are quite a few "if – then" statements.

Scan the verses listed below and look for the word "if" **or** a contradicting statement. Note what you find in the lines below:

1. Verse: 1... If: _____ Then: _____

2. Verse: 3... If: _____ Then: _____

3. Verse: 4... If: _____ But: _____

   Then: _____ And: _____

4. Verse: 5... If: _____ Then: _____

   And: _____

5. Verse: 6... If: _____ Then:_____

6. Verse: 9/11... If: _____ Then: _____

But: _____

7. Verse: 10... If: _____ But: _____

Then: _____ And: _____

8. Verse: 15... If: _____ Then: _____

9. Verse: 17... If: _____ Then: _____

10. Verse: 19... If: _____ Then: _____

11. Verse: 24... If: _____ Then: _____

12. Verse: 29... If: _____ Then: _____

A.C.T.S. PRAYER TIME

"My son, keep my words, and lay up my commandments with thee. Keep my commandments, and live; and my law as the apple of thine eye."
~ Proverbs 7:1-2 KJV ~

A - Adoration_____

C - Confession_____

T - Thanksgiving_____

S - Supplication_____

"You must pray with all your might. That does not mean saying your prayers, or sitting gazing about in church or chapel with eyes wide open while someone else says them for you. It means fervent, effectual, untiring wrestling with God. This kind of prayer be sure the devil and the world and your own indolent, unbelieving nature will oppose. They will pour water on this flame."
~ William Booth ~

DIGGING DEEPER

Re-read 1 John 2:18. Note that John says we have heard that the antichrist is coming and that even now many antichrists have appeared. So, he has noted two different characters here:

There is an Antichrist and there are others who have attributes like the Antichrist.

Look up the following passages and summarize the additional information you learn about both.

1 John 2:22: _____

_____

2 John 7: _____

_____

Daniel 7:7: _____

_____

DAY FIVE

ON MY KNEES:

The weeks are flying by! Once again we find ourselves at the end of a week and midway through another chapter of 1 John. Be encouraged, faithful student of the Word. Your work in the Word is noteworthy! Continue in your training, for the battle is raging and you are one of the Lord's trustworthy soldiers. Begin your time in the Word with prayer.

Pray. "Master, Savior, Lord of my heart, I come before you today in hopeful expectation of hearing from you through the words of John in 1 John. Open my ears, soften my heart and awaken my mind to the things You want me to act on. I want to be a faithful bondservant and strong warrior. Train me through Your Law. In Jesus' Name, I pray, amen."

Write. As you write 1 John 2:14-16 behind the "Write!" tab of your Sword Study today, dwell on the words. Think about what the Word enables us to overcome.

Read. Wait! Don't open your Bible yet…read on.

INVESTIGATIVE STUDY
STREETVIEW: CHAPTER 2

Apply!

Searching for a couple exhortations, defining a few, potentially unfamiliar words and choosing Key Words are on the task list for today! We will wait to read the chapter again until we choose our Key Words for Chapter 2.

First, John throws a couple of exhortations in the text to his readers. An exhortation is a strong directive to act. It is as if John is suddenly reminded of something dangerous and wants to make certain that his children are warned. What a beautiful picture of fatherly love and discipleship, both of which flow naturally from this dear man of God. Remember, the easiest way to find an exhortation is to search for an action verb!

1. **Verse 15**: Verb: _____ Exhortation: _____

2. **Verse 24**: Verb: _____ Exhortation: _____

3. **Verse 28**: Verb: _____ Exhortation: _____

Next, John gives us a list to describe the attributes of the "world" in verses 16 and 17. On the lines below, jot down all that you learn about recognizing the characteristics of world.

1. _____

2. _____

3. _____

4. _____

Using a Bible dictionary or online tool, quickly paraphrase a definition for the words below:

Advocate: _____

Propitiation: _____

Abide: _____

Grab a set of colored pencils and/or a few highlighters. Today, instead of slowly reading the second chapter of 1 John, skim through the verses. Look for repeating words – the word "write" should rise to the top of the list for certain! Mark each word that you feel is important in a unique way. Make sure to mark all the references to God using our provided symbols.

On the lines below, note the words that you would want to study further:

_____

_____

_____

_____

A . C . T . S .   P R A Y E R   T I M E

"Do not store up for yourselves treasures on earth, where
moth and rust destroy, and where thieves break in and steal."
~ Matthew 6:19 NASB ~

A - *Adoration*_____

C - *Confession*_____

T - *Thanksgiving*_____

S - *Supplication*_____

"Every professing Christian is the soldier of Christ. He is bound … to fight Christ's battle against sin, the world and the devil. The man that does not do this breaks his vow. He is a spiritual defaulter. He does not fulfill the engagements made for him. The man that does not do this is practically renouncing his Christianity. The very fact that he belongs to a church, attends a Christian place of worship, and calls himself a Christian, is a public declaration that he desires to be reckoned a soldier of Jesus Christ."
~ *J.C. Ryle* ~

DIGGING DEEPER

Find a quiet time this weekend and re-read the whole book of 1 John.

Samuel Morris: Light Out of the Jungle
(Conclusion of speech given at Taylor University Convocation, September 9, 1892)

Some may find my story hard to believe. But some months later in a city near the coast of Africa, I met a boy who belonged to the enemy tribe. This young man had been present at the time of my capture and escape. "We did not know what had happened," he told me. "A bright light flashed over you. We heard someone call your name, and then you disappeared." After I explained the miracle, he decided to follow Christ, too.

Eager to learn more about God, I still had many questions. I decided to travel to America to expand my knowledge. I searched along the eastern African coast until I found a ship bound for America, but the captain refused to take me aboard. I begged God to change his heart. How could I have been surprised when He did?

Although I didn't know anything about ships, I was hired to take the place of a sailor who had fallen ill. The captain and his sailors drank too much and often treated me terribly. They beat me and assigned me the most difficult tasks. One tried to kill me. But I kept showing them the love of God, and before we landed on the shores of America, many of them—including the captain—had trusted Christ as their Savior.

When we arrived in New York City, I spent many months with Stephen Merritt, a man my missionary friend in Africa had said could teach me more. Stephen, a pastor, ran a homeless mission, and my desire to know God helped stir the hearts of the men there. Many became Christians.

As I spent time studying the Scriptures with Stephen, I found myself growing in the knowledge of God, right in line with my prayers. "You're moving from head knowledge (what you can know by sight and perception) to heart knowledge," Stephen said. "That's something you understand only by faith, deep within your spirit."

Along with the men of the homeless shelter, I was learning to abide in Christ, to remain with Him. This meant He had the freedom to rearrange any part of my life or character. I was not the same man I was back in Africa, nor was I the same man who landed in America. The Lord was growing and shaping me. I knew and believed the love He had for me (1 John 4:16). And without Him, I could do nothing.

Still, I wanted to know God more. "Go to Taylor University," Stephen urged. Dean Thaddeus Reade wanted me to come, too. In fact, he started an account to pay for my education that became known as the Samuel Faith Fund.

In December of 1891, I arrived here in Fort Wayne. When Dean Reade asked me which room I wanted, I told him the truth: "If there is a room nobody wants, give that to me."

I spent most of my evenings in that room talking to my Father, which most of you would call praying. Since I came to know Christ in that deeper way, it all seemed so simple. Like the apostle Paul, the great desire of my heart was to know Him more.

God used this desire to touch and transform the lives of the people who surrounded me. Local churches often invited me, their "missionary in ebony," to speak. I felt honored to share my story and was surprised when a local newspaper covered an all-night prayer service we held. It included the story of my capture and conversion, so almost everyone in the area grew to recognize the name Samuel Morris.

Likewise, the "Samuel Faith Fund" continued to grow as more and more donations came in. Soon, it held so much that Dean Reade could use it to help other needy students, too. A spiritual revival began in the town.

And that is where we find ourselves today. We are, as a town, a community and a college, longing to know Him more. We don't want to stay content with head-knowledge. We want to go beyond the facts.

Will you seek Him with me? Will you know and believe the love He has for you? I will be glad to speak with you in private, because I know He is longing to know you more.

Postscript: On May 12, 1893, Samuel Morris died after contracting a severe cold. His body never grew accustomed to the temperatures in America. But his death inspired many of his fellow students to serve as missionaries to Africa and fulfill his dream of one day returning to minister to his people. Today, Taylor University is still sending out missionaries, thanks more than a little to the life of a man of faith named Samuel Morris.

D A Y   O N E

ON MY KNEES:

How easy it is to get wrapped up in the things of this world! They are constantly flashing "Important!" and "Do this NOW!" Ah, but the things of the world will pass away. What are the eternal things? What will last forever? The grass withers and the flower fades, according to Isaiah 40:8, but the Word of our God stands forever! We will hear more about eternal things from John today as well, but first go to our God in prayer.

Pray. "Lord, there are many calls for my attention. I want to focus on You and Your Word now. Please drown out the noise and distractions so that I can hear You clearly. Show me where I need to change and be more like Jesus."

Write. As you write 1 John 2:17-19 in your copy of 1 John, highlight what lives forever in Verse 17.

Read. Once again, read through the second chapter of 2 John.

Apply!

INVESTIGATIVE STUDY
UNDER THE RUG:
WORD STUDY - "KNOW"

We closed our study last week by marking all the repetitive and theme words in 1 John 2. Today, we are going to begin an in-depth look at one of the Key Words in Chapter 2; actually, it is a Key Word for the entire book of 1 John. The Greek words *eido* and *ginosko* are used over 30 times in John's small letter. Their meanings are different levels of the word, *know* (knoweth, known). Did you mark this word? Look at the two sentences below:

"I *know* the President because I **saw** his picture in the newspaper."

"I *know* the President because I was his **personal** assistant for 10 years."

The two Greek words John uses are both translated "know" in English. The first Greek word, *eido*, means a surface knowledge of someone or something, similar to "see" or "perceive." The second, *ginosko*, means to have a growing, deepening personal knowledge of someone. How amazing to watch John effectively use these two words to show us the differences between true Christianity and the false teaching of the Gnostics! We will see how John used different Greek words to make sure we knew what he meant.

Read through the 2 steps of the Word Studies of *know*. Then, we will examine how John used these two words.

PART A: If you were to look up the word *know* in Strong's Concordance, you would find the Strong's numbers assigned to it are 1097 and 1492. Note this, because you will use these numbers to look up a detailed explanation of the original Greek words in Part B. Below is the transliteration, the pronunciations, and the basic definitions from Strong's lexicon for each of the Greek words:

> **1492. *Know*.** eido, *I'-do*; a primary verb, consider, have knowledge, look on, perceive, see.

> **1097. *Know*,** ginosko, *ghin-oce-ko*, be aware of, perceive, understand, be sure.

PART B: Next, if you look up the numbers **1097** and **1492** in another Greek lexicon, you can discover more detailed explanations of the word in Greek.

1492. Know:

   1.   to see
   2.   to know, be acquainted with
   3.   Sense of perceiving an absolute truth

1097. Know:

   1.   To know in complete sense; deeply
   >   a. to perceive, observe, obtain a knowledge of or insight
   >   into. It denotes a personal and true relation between
   >   the person knowing and the object known, that is to say,
   >   to be influenced by one's knowledge of the object.
   2.   Process of deepening one's knowledge, knowledge from deeply
   >   seeking
   3.   To know by experience

PART C: First, there are two verses in 1 John that use both of our Greek words for *know*.

> "If ye *know* (see) that he is righteous, *ye know* (deeply) that every one that doeth righteousness is born of God." 1 John 2:29

> "And we *know* (see) that the Son of God is come; and hath given us an under standing, that we may *know* (deeply)…" 1 John 5:20

Next, let's take a look at a few of the various verses that used *eido* with a Believer's general knowledge. Look up and read the following passages, then to help cement your understanding, we would like you put the letter "*S*" for "see" in the margin of your Bible or above the word "*know*" in your Bible.

1 John 2:11	1 John 3:15
1 John 2:20	1 John 5:13
1 John 2:21 (both instances)	1 John 5:15 (both instances)

Now, do the same exercise with the verses that used *ginosko* meaning deep knowledge or understanding. Use a caret (^) and insert the word "deeply" before the word "*know*" in each of the following passages.

1 John 2:3 (both instances)	1 John 3:24
1 John 2:4	1 John 4:2
1 John 2:18	1 John 4:6
1 John 2:29	1 John 4:7

In summary, when John uses *eido* (1492), he is speaking of a general knowledge, one that has an elementary understanding.

Whereas, when he uses the word *ginosko* (1097), he is speaking of the process of actively deepening or a deep, experiential knowledge. A simplified example would be that of the difference between an acquaintance and a dear friend. When we study the Word, we begin to deeply *know* Him, and our walk and lifestyle begin to reflect Him.

APPLY!

Cover the picture on the next page with your hand! Don't look at it! Now, when we say, uncover the picture. Look at it for 10 seconds, no longer. Ready? Ok, look at the picture for 10 seconds and then cover it with your non-writing hand.

What did you see in your first glance of 10 seconds?

_____

_____

Now, uncover the picture again and study it. Describe all that you see on the lines below:

_____

_____

_____

_____

_____

Did you notice how much more you *knew* when you studied the picture than when you took a quick glance? To move from an aquaintance to a deep, intimate relationship with God, we must actively seek to know Him by spending time with Him in His Word. Then, we will deeply *know* Him and His ways.

A.C.T.S. PRAYER TIME

A - *Adoration*_____

C - *Confession*_____

T - *Thanksgiving*_____

S - *Supplication*_____

DIGGING DEEPER

Here are the remaining uses of the Greek words for **know** in 1 John. Complete the insertion of "see" and "deeply" for each.

1492. *Eido* (See)

1 John 3:2	1 John 5:18
1 John 3:5	1 John 5:19
1 John 3:14	

1097. *Ginosko* (Deeply)

1 John 2:5	1 John 3:20
1 John 2:13 (both instances)	1 John 4:13
1 John 2:14	1 John 4:16
1 John 3:1 (both instances)	1 John 5:2
1 John 3:6	

D A Y   T W O

ON MY KNEES:

A new day has arrived with new opportunities of choice throughout. It is wonderful that you are sitting here ready to begin your day with the Lord's perspective. Our God calls us through His Word to know Him. Child of God, draw near to Him in prayer before you begin studying His words.

Pray. "Father, God, I want to know You in a way that is far beyond a "surface, faraway" knowledge. Help me to press on and forge forward in today's study. Show me how to know You more through the Scripture today. Revive my heart!"

Write. Please open up to the "Write!" section of your Sword Study. Today, let's write 1 John 2:20-23.

Read. Today, read both Chapters 1 and 2 of 1 John.

Apply!

INVESTIGATIVE STUDY
UNDER THE RUG:
CROSS REFERENCES - "KNOW"

Deeply *knowing* God is one the core goals of the Bible. He has provided, throughout the Scripture, the key to eternal fellowship with Him. Our small book of 1 John contains over 30 uses of the word *know*. Today, we will look at a variety of passages to gain a better picture of the importance of *ginosko* and its Hebrew counterpart, *yada* (Strong's 3045). Ready?

Look up and read Exodus 5:1-2.

Who, mockingly, said the word *know* in this passage? _____

To whom did he say the word *know*? _____

Was there a desire to *know* God? _____

Look up and read Job 21:7-15.

Who said the word *know/knowledge*? _____

Was there a desire to *know* God? _____

Look up and read Psalm 25:14-16. (Note: "Shew" is *make known* in the King James Version)

Who receives **knowledge**? _____

Who gives the **knowledge**? _____

Was there a desire to **know** God? _____

Look up and read Psalm 36:7-10*.

Who receives lovingkindness/love? _____

Where do they see the light? _____

What else do the 'upright in heart' receive? _____

Look up and read Hosea 6:3-6*.

How is one directed to **know** God in this passage (v. 3)? _____

What is desired more than sacrifice and burnt offerings (v. 6)? _____

What is the result of knowing God (v. 3)? _____

Look up and read John 17:3*.

What is eternal life? _____

Look up and read Philippians 3:8-11*.

What is held as the highest priority for Paul in this passage? _____

What is everything else to him? _____

Why does he want to **know** Jesus? _____

Look up and read Exodus 33:13.

Complete the following prayer that Moses prayed:
If I have: _____
Then: _____
So that: _____
So that: _____

As you hear Moses' thought process for *knowing* and pleasing the Lord, does it make you want *know* Him? Use his words to lead you into your A.C.T.S. prayer as you close your time in the Word.

A.C.T.S. PRAYER TIME

*"I have not departed from the commandment of His lips; I have treasured
the words of His mouth More than my necessary food."*
~ Job 23:12 NKJV ~

A - *Adoration* _____

C - *Confession* _____

T - *Thanksgiving* _____

S - *Supplication* _____

D A Y   T H R E E

On My Knees:

Sit down. Relax. Take a long, drawn-out breath and realize that this is such a good way to start your day. Coming to the Lord for His wisdom and strength is what will carry you through each day. When we trust in our own understanding and strength, we will falter. We just can't do it on our own. What a blessing that we have a friend, confidant and guide in our God. Begin with prayer.

Pray. "Lord, how I love Your presence. Where else can I turn and know that I will be loved for exactly who I am? You are gracious and full of mercy. Please show me where I may be in error, for I do not want to displease You in any way or take your kindness for granted. Convict me on any unconfessed sin in my life. I want to keep short accounts and not sever our fellowship. Shed light on the passages that I am about to study. Amen."

Write. Turn to the "Write!" section of your study and copy 1 John 2:24-26 on the page.

Read. Find a sibling. Call a grandparent. Speed-dial a friend. Together, read 1 John 2. Make the time short, just enough to read with one another and maybe even pray – and then carry on with your study.

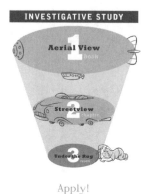

INVESTIGATIVE STUDY

Apply!

INVESTIGATIVE STUDY
UNDER THE RUG:
Word Study - "Abide"

When we want to get to know someone, we spend time with them. The more time we spend with them, the more like them we become. John uses the word *abide* to relay this message to us. Let's look at the meaning of *abide* in Greek.

PART A: If you were to look up the word *abide* in Strong's Concordance, you would find that the Strong's number assigned to it in 1 John is number 3306. We will use this number to look up the detailed explanation of the Greek words in Part B. Below are the transliteration (the way the word is written in English), the pronunciation, and the basic definition from the Strong's lexicon (dictionary).

3306. *Abide.* m□nō, *men□-o,* a primary verb; to stay (in a given place, state, relation or expectancy): - abide, continue, dwell, endure, be present, remain, stand, tarry (for), thine own.

PART B: If you look up the number **3306** in another Greek lexicon, you can discover further explanations of the meaning of *abide* in Greek as seen here:

1)   to remain, dwell, live

    a.   In a place

    b.   In a state or condition

    c.   One person remains

          i.   With another in something, to remain united with him in heart, mind and will.

          ii.   With something by persevering, remaining steadfast

PART C: When we review the use of *abide* in 1 John we find that John primarily uses the word in relation to letter c, with one person remaining with another or with something. Although, in 1 John 3:14, he is referring to a specific state or condition that a person is dwelling in. Look up the verse to understand how he does this.

Next, we will look at the other uses and determine if John uses *abide* with another person or with a situation. Turn to each of the passages and write "Person" next to those who fall under the letter "i" and "Something" next to those who fall under the letter "ii" (King James Version uses the word "dwell."

1 John 2:10: Person _____ Something (What is it? _____)

1 John 2:14: Person _____ Something (What is it? _____)

1 John 2:17: Person _____ Something (What is it? _____)

1 John 2:19: Person _____ Something (What is it? _____)

1 John 3:24: Person _____ Something (What is it? _____)

1 John 4:12: Person _____ Something (What is it? _____)

1 John 4:13: Person _____ Something (What is it? _____)

1 John 4:15: Person _____ Something (What is it? _____)

1 John 4:16: Person _____ Something (What is it? _____)

May you continue to *abide* with fellow believers and remain steadfast in His Word as you walk through the rest of your day. Finish up by spending time in prayer.

A.C.T.S. PRAYER TIME

"For the Lord gives wisdom; from His mouth come knowledge and understanding; He stores up sound wisdom for the upright; He is a shield to those who walk uprightly;"
~ Proverbs 2:6-7 NKJV ~

A - *Adoration* _____

C - *Confession* _____

T - *Thanksgiving* _____

S - *Supplication* _____

DAY FOUR

ON MY KNEES:

"It is great to be in someone's thoughts, but even better to be in their prayers." How true is this statement? Man's thoughts are subpar compared to our ability to call on our all-powerful God on the behalf of another or for ourselves. As you go to the Lord in prayer today, remember to ask for strength, not only for yourself, but for your accountability partners and family members as well.

Pray. "You are my Rock and my mighty Fortress, Lord. Today, I ask for your wisdom and strength for both myself and those around me as we come to study Your Word. Enlighten us and show us how to walk in righteousness. Help us not grow weary or give up fellowshipping with You or one another. Draw us close, Lord. In Jesus' name, amen."

Write. As you write 1 John 2:27-29, stop and read John's words out loud.

Read. As we near the end of our study of 1 John, Chapter 2, once again turn your focus, as you read, to the reason we study the Word of God… to know Him!

INVESTIGATIVE STUDY

Aerial View 1 book

Streetview 2

Under the Rug 3 word

Apply!

INVESTIGATIVE STUDY
UNDER THE RUG:
CROSS REFERENCES - "ABIDE"

Being united for a single purpose with another can be so encouraging; it can also be fun at times, and vital in other situations or circumstances.

Come, seek out these passages as they expand and expound our understanding of the word *abide*. Note what you learn on the line after each reference. Don't leave any lines blank just because you feel that you haven't learned something new or significant. Allow the Lord to reinforce His words, whether new or old insights, by completing this exercise.

Read Psalm 15:1-5.

Wow! List all of the characteristics of those who *abide* with the Lord and as a result are not shaken.

_____   _____
_____   _____
_____   _____
_____   _____
_____

What do you learn about *abide* in Psalm 61:4-7? _____

Why don't we have to *abide* (remain) in darkness according to John 12:46? _____
_____

Look up and read John 8:31-32*.

Who are Jesus' disciples? _____

What do His disciples *know*? _____

What does this *knowledge* accomplish for the disciples? _____

Read, then summarize what you learn in the following passages.

John 14:16-17 _____

John 15:4-10 _____

2 John 9-10 _____

A.C.T.S. PRAYER TIME

"The LORD is my strength and my song, and he has become my salvation; this is my God, and I will praise him, my father's God, and I will exalt him."
~ Exodus 15:2 NASB ~

A - Adoration _____

C - Confession _____

T - Thanksgiving _____

S - Supplication _____

DIGGING DEEPER

John 15:4-10 is full of the word *abide*. Do a mini-Sword Study of this incredible passage. Write the passage on a separate piece of paper and highlight each occurrence of *abide*. Write your own questions and answers using the passage.

DAY FIVE

ON MY KNEES:

We are finishing up another week and chapter of 1 John. How wonderful and excellent is the Word of God! Here we find God stories, answers to our hearts' questions and a love beyond compare. Most importantly, we find Jesus as our Advocate for an eternal relationship with the Father. Come before Him now, in humble adoration and confession to begin the day's fellowship in His Word.

Pray. "How excellent is Your name! Lord of ages, King of eternity, I come before You in reverence and worship. You are Holy and I am not. Help me to walk in Your Spirit today and stray neither to the left nor to the right. Illuminate my path with Your words and gentle prodding. I want to focus on You and not myself or others. Thank You for forgiving me of my unrighteousness. Amen."

Read. Quietly read 1 John, Chapter 2.

INVESTIGATIVE STUDY

Aerial View book 1

Streetview chapter 2

Under the Rug 3

Apply!

INVESTIGATIVE STUDY
1-2-3 SUMMARIZE: CHAPTER 2

Have you been looking forward to doing the Diagram throughout the week? Remember, if you have any issues figuring out how to fill in your Day 10 Diagram, talk to a parent; their Guidebook includes a key to this diagram.

☐ To begin, look at the top of the Day 10 Diagram. Fill in the chapter number. Look at Week 1, Day 5 for the original title you created for 1 John 2. Review what you wrote and refine your title with the new insights that you have learned over the last 10 days.

☐ Next, which verse from the chapter do you think was the "key verse?"

☐ On the right of the page, transfer your key Greek words from this chapter. Write the English words on the top line after the words "Greek Words." Transfer the Greek spellings and write a short definition of their meanings.

☐ On the bottom of the Diagram page, transfer the most important things that you learned about God through marking the references about Him on your "Write!" pages.

Let's continue walking along with John and our fellow travelers as we fill in this next Day 10 Diagram. In Chapter 2, John identified the recipients of his letter and gave his reasons for writing to them. Underneath each person in the diagram, label one of the three groups to which John was writing. Then, on the blanks to the right of John and the young Christians, list out John's stated reasons for writing to that group. Finally, on the left of each person, label the appropriate description that John says should characterize that group of recipients. (Hints: John is carrying a Bible, the young man has a walking stick, and the young lady has a heart next to her feet.)

If John's recipients (and we) are faithful to God's exhortations in John's letter, then we will not be captured in the destructive trap of loving the world. In the center of the circle that represents the world system, write "The World" under the crossed-out heart. In the other four blanks within the circle, list the attributes that John notes about the world in 1 John 2:16-17.

Above the deceptive lure of the world system, the cross stands strong and true. In Chapter 2, John said that Jesus is our _____ when we sin; write this title for Jesus at the top of the cross. At the shining foot of the cross, note once again that "God is Light." How good it is to know that we have been freed from the world and can walk in the light with God!

A . C . T . S .   P R A Y E R   T I M E

"But the path of the righteous is like the light of dawn,
which shines brighter and brighter until full day."
~ Proverbs 4:18 ESV ~

A - Adoration_____

C - Confession_____

T - Thanksgiving_____

S - Supplication_____

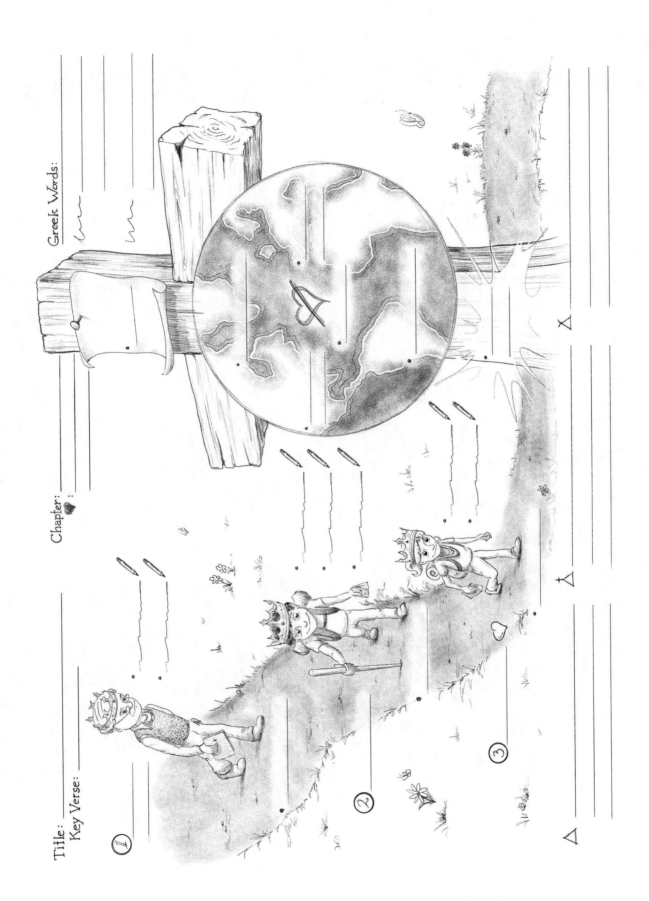

Title: _____
Key Verse: _____

Chapter: ___ : ___

Greek Words: _____

Billy Graham: Light to the Nations

November 1, 1934

I don't keep up with my journal as often as I should, but I wanted to be sure and record something today. Today, this old (I'll be sixteen in a few days) farm boy from Charlotte, North Carolina made a decision that will change my life forever: I received Christ as my Lord and Savior. Instead of calling religion "hogwash," as I did not long ago, I'm a child of God!

What does that mean? At this point, I'm not exactly sure—at least not in terms of how it affects my daily life. I do know that our visiting preacher, Mordecai Ham, explained the beauty of heaven and the reality of hell. He told us if we died without accepting Christ's death on the cross as the substitute for our sin, we'd end up separated from God forever.

I've always thought the Bible was true. I just never thought it applied to me. But tonight when Rev. Ham explained, it all seemed crystal-clear. It made the hours I've spent in the hayloft reading books seem nothing more than a waste of time. This one book, this precious old Book, is the one that matters most.

I received Jesus today, and I know my life will never be the same.

February 15, 1939

Today marked another milestone in my walk with Christ. That's because the St. John's River Council (a group of Baptist pastors) here in Tampa, Florida ordained me. Now, I'm set apart as a minister of the gospel, commissioned to spread His light.

More than two years ago, I first sensed the Lord calling me to preach. Like

Moses, I fought it, thinking up all kinds of excuses. But God persisted. One night more than a year ago, as I walked the eighteenth green of the Temple Terrace Golf Course, the Holy Spirit overtook me. I dropped to my knees and cried, "Oh God, if You want me to preach, I will serve You."

The council asked many questions about what I believe and why. It was a good thing I had my answers all ready, because I was too nervous to think and just blurted out whatever came to mind. But those answers must have been pretty close to right, because the council approved me. I guess the good Lord was giving His child words to speak, just like the Scripture says.

I haven't written in my journal for some time. I stay so busy studying that I'm having a hard time keeping up. My school is called the Florida Bible Institute. Until this year, I was enrolled at Bob Jones University, but I feel so much more at home here.

My intention, unless God shows me otherwise, is to graduate from this fine institution and then head to Illinois and finish out my education at Wheaton College. Nothing can stop me now!

June 10, 1943

I'm just a few days away from receiving my degree in anthropology from Wheaton. To say the least, it's been an enlightening four years. And one of the biggest lights has been a young lady, Miss Ruth Bell. She and I intend to be married later this summer. What's so special about her?

Everything. Before I met her, I heard about her from a friend. He told me *that besides being the most beautiful girl he'd ever met, she got up every morning at four to pray. She grew up as a missionary kid in China and has a heart for the lost.*

A girl like that sounded too good for me, and too good to be true. But once I met her, I knew I wanted to see more of her.

On our first date, we went to see Handel's Messiah. And it didn't take long after that for both of us to realize God had a "Hallelujah" for us in each other.

We don't know everything that lies ahead. But we do know we want to spend the rest of our days together. Thank You, Lord, for giving me Ruth. "He finds a wife finds a good thing and receives favor from the Lord" (Prov. 18:22).

December 5, 1949

My life seems to be changing once again. For a short time, I pastured a small Baptist church in Illinois. Ruth and I were happy there, but the Lord called us to a different kind of service.

I started traveling and leading meetings for Youth for Christ, an organization created to tell servicemen returning from the War and other young people about God. Before long, my fame as an evangelist started to spread. I wanted to see more people move from the kingdom of darkness to light, from living as children of the devil to new life as children of God. Along the way, I kept preaching at various churches, revival services and crusades.

Not long ago, a group, "Christ for Greater Los Angeles," invited me to preach at their Los Angeles crusade. God moved, and what started as a three-

week revival continued for an additional five weeks. I know the Lord is moving me toward a life as an evangelist.

Still, I dread the publicity associated with these events. I've been preaching crusades for long enough to understand that you can't manufacture the Holy Spirit. He's the One who draws people to the Father. And He's the One who makes us His children.

Forever.

Enjoy more excerpts from Billy Graham's life and ministry next week!

DAY ONE

ON MY KNEES:

Chapter 3 of 1 John will become our focus over the next two weeks. Are you excited to see what God will reveal to you? Or, are you unsure if you feel like continuing this study? Turn to the Lord and share how you are feeling today.

Pray. "Omniscient God and Father, even though You know my heart and thoughts, You ask me to come and share them with You. I want to be excited to sit at Your feet, yet I confess that at times it is hard to come when there are other things to do. Impress on my heart the importance of our time together. Make this next chapter of 1 John speak to me in ways that I know You are talking to me personally. Show me where I need to change and be more like You than like me. In Your precious name, I pray, amen."

Write. Grab a red pen or pencil so that you will have it nearby as you copy 1 John 3 into your "Write!" pages. Each time you write the word "love" use your red pen either to write the word, or to mark a red heart above or around it. Begin with verses 1 and 2 today.

Read. Open your Bible to 1 John 3 and read the chapter.

Apply!

INVESTIGATIVE STUDY
STREETVIEW: CHAPTER 3

Time to turn the tables! As we approach a new chapter of 1 John, we would like you to write a question for each verse in Chapter 3. We have given you two lines so that you can also write your answers on the second line in a different color. Make sure to create questions that the verse can answer itself. Place a star next to your favorite so that you can share it with your family later this week at your Family Bonfire.

Verse 1: _____

Answer: _____

Verse 2: _____

Answer: _____

Verse 3: _____

Answer: _____

Verse 4: _____

Answer: _____

Verse 5: _____

Answer: _____

Verse 6: _____

Answer: _____

Verse 7: _____

Answer: _____

Verse 8: _____

Answer: _____

Verse 9: _____

Answer: _____

Verse 10: _____

Answer: _____

Verse 11: _____

Answer: _____

Verse 12: _____

Answer: _____

Good job! Tomorrow, we will finish the rest of Chapter 3's verses. Use the verse question and answer that you starred as the foundation for your closing prayer time with the Lord.

A.C.T.S. PRAYER TIME

"No soldier gets entangled in civilian pursuits, since
his aim is to please the one who enlisted him."
~ 2 Timothy 2:4 ESV ~

A - *Adoration* _____

C - *Confession* _____

T - *Thanksgiving* _____

S - *Supplication* _____

D A Y   T W O

ON MY KNEES:

"Amazing love! How can it be that You, my King, should die for me. Amazing love and I know it is true – it is my joy to honor you in all I do." We have begun to see how great the Father's love is for us in our study of 1 John. His amazing love has enabled us to call Him "Father." The King of kings, Lord of lords, Creator of ALL things can be our Father through belief in the provision of Jesus. Take the time before you begin meeting with Him in His Word to sing a song to Him in prayer.

Pray. Sing a song of His love: "Amazing Grace," "Amazing Love," "Lord, I Love You," … or you chose one!

Write. Now, write verses 3-4 of 1 John 3.

Read. Quietly, but out loud, read 1 John 3 again.

INVESTIGATIVE STUDY

Aerial View
ZOOM

1

Streetview
chapter

2

Under the Rug

3

Apply!

INVESTIGATIVE STUDY
STREETVIEW: CHAPTER 3

Did you notice how writing questions for each verse makes you truly listen to what is being said in each verse? Today, we will finish creating questions and answers for the remaining Chapter 3 verses. Make sure to write complete sentences in your answers, using the Scripture's words.

Verse 13: _____

Answer: _____

Verse 14: _____

Answer: _____

Verse 15: _____

Answer: _____

Verse 16: _____

Answer: _____

Verse 17: _____

Answer: _____

Verse 18: _____

Answer: _____

Verse 19: _____

Answer: _____

Verse 20: _____

Answer: _____

Verse 21: _____

Answer: _____

Verse 22: _____

Answer: _____

Verse 23: _____

Answer: _____

Verse 24: _____

Answer: _____

APPLY!

"Praise him with the timbrel and dance: praise him with stringed instruments and organs. Praise him upon the loud cymbals: praise him upon the high sounding cymbals. Let everything that hath breath praise the Lord. Praise ye the Lord."
Psalm 150:4-6 (KJV)

What talent or talents has the Lord given you? Can you play the piano? Cymbals? Take the time today to worship the Lord through song. If you are not musically inclined, simply put on a pair of earphones, turn on your favorite songs of praise. Go to a secluded place and sing unto the Lord!

A.C.T.S. PRAYER TIME

A - *Adoration*_____

C - *Confession*_____

T - *Thanksgiving*_____

S - *Supplication*_____

DAY THREE

ON MY KNEES:

God's creation cries out evidences of Him. Just as the fact that the digits in the multiples of nine equal nine when added together is a special evidence for the math-minded person, and the giant gentleness of the Clydesdale gives additional proof of His existence for the animal lover, we can see Him in our days the more we abide in Him through His Word. What a glorious blessing to know that God reveals more and more of Himself through His Word and that the newness will never end! Start your day with Him in proclaiming Him, or the rocks will! (Luke 19:40)

Pray. "Creator, Sustainer and Master Planner, Your works are wondrous and greatly to be praised, but certainly not more than You, Yourself. Thank You for giving me examples of Your power and existence everywhere I turn. From the creatures, to nature, to my mind, I can witness Your supremacy. May I see You more today than I could yesterday. Amen."

Write. 1 John 3:5-7 is your next set of verses to write in "My Copy of 1 John".

Read. Take a moment, go outside with your Bible and read 1 John 3. Leave everything else in its spot.

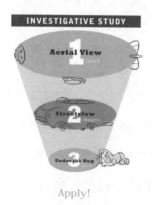

Apply!

INVESTIGATIVE STUDY
STREETVIEW: CHAPTER 3

As you questioned the 3rd chapter of 1 John, did you notice that John added to the description of the recipients? We cannot brush over this new addition- it is significant and noteworthy. He has called us sons, or children, of God! Yes, he claims there is an invitation to us to be adopted into the family of God. How amazing! How incredible! We are invited not to be just friends or second-cousins-once-removed, but to be a part of the Royal family! We can be adopted as sons and daughters of God with full birthright privileges.

Today, we are going to look at the characteristics of the children of God and tomorrow, we will investigate their counterparts, the children of the devil.

Let's look at the 1 John passages and other related Scriptures to make certain that we understand what the Lord was saying through John's words. As you travel to other Scriptures, be sure to keep a pencil or bookmark in 1 John 3, as your home base.

Children (Sons) of God

According to 1 John 3:1, what attribute of the Father is bestowed when He calls us sons of God?

_____

What did that love do, according to John 3:16?

_____

When did God display His love for us, according to Romans 5:8?

_____

Who can call themselves children of God, according to John 1:12?

_____

As sons of God, who will we be like, and when, according to 1 John 3:2?

_____

Who is pure, according to 1 John 3:3?

_____

What does the child of God do, according to verse 3?

_____

Romans 8:14-17 reveals the power behind our ability to walk as sons of God. Summarize all that you learn from this passage:

_____

_____

How does Galatians 6:10 give you direction in regard to how to treat other children of God?

_____

What are the children of God to do with the children of the devil according to Luke 6:34-35?

_____

Look up and read Matthew 5:9. Who are children of God, according to this verse?

_____

Back in 1 John 3, verses 6 and 9 speak of practicing sin. Why don't the sons of God practice sin?

_____

According to 1 John 3:10, what are two characteristics of the children of God?

_____

What, in verse 13, should the sons of God expect from the world?

_____

Verses 14 through 17 describe a trademark of the child of God. Summarize what you learn from these verses:

_____

_____

John qualifies the son of God in verse 23. What are the two key commandments for the child of God, according to this verse?

_____

What have the children of God done, according to 1 John 2:13-14?

_____

APPLY!

Whether you know them or not, surely there is someone within your church who is in need. If your family doesn't personally know someone, go and ask your church office. Spearhead this project for your family. Purpose to do more than just one meal or task for them. Plan to commit to helping them for a season. Bake a meal each week, care for their children, give them a restaurant gift card, or your whole family can work with them on their yard. You can bring the carload of flower flats! Present your ideas at your Family Bonfire.

A.C.T.S. PRAYER TIME

Every day will I bless thee; and I will praise thy name for ever and ever. Great is the Lord, and greatly to be praised; and his greatness is unsearchable. One generation shall <u>praise thy works to another,</u> and shall declare thy mighty acts. I will speak of the glorious honour of thy majesty, and of thy wondrous works. And men shall speak of the might of thy terrible acts: and I will de-clare thy greatness. They shall abundantly utter the memory of thy great goodness, and shall sing of thy righteousness. The Lord is gracious, and full of compassion; slow to anger, and of great mercy. The Lord is good to all: and his tender mercies are over all his works. All thy works shall praise thee, O Lord; and thy saints shall bless thee."
~ Psalm 145:1-10 KJV ~

Using this powerful Psalm, close your time in the Word of God, and with the Word, Jesus.

A - *Adoration*_____

C - *Confession*_____

T - *Thanksgiving*_____

S - *Supplication*_____

DAY FOUR

ON MY KNEES:

Did you get enough rest last night? Are you weary from all the activities on your schedule? God beckons us in His Word to "come" and He "will give us rest" when we have labored and are burdened. Go to Him in prayer, for there you will surely find rest.

Pray. "Lord, my life can seem overwhelming and heavy. Oh, how great it would be to really rest in You. You say that Your yoke is easy and burden is light, but I feel as though things are hard and overbearing. Even as I pray those words, I realize that I must be depending upon my ways rather than Yours. As I study Your Word and see Your ways today, help me to live them out. In Your powerful name, I pray. Amen"

Write. Turn to 1 John 3 and write verses 8 through 10.

Read. Grab a younger sibling or child and read 1 John, Chapter 3 together. Then, invite him or her to complete today's Sword Study lesson nearby.

INVESTIGATIVE STUDY

Aerial View 1
Streetview 2
Under the Rug 3

Apply!

INVESTIGATIVE STUDY
STREETVIEW: CHAPTER 3

How does a non-Believer act? How can I recognize a lost person? Today, we will investigate the children of the devil. First, we will review John's descriptions within 1 John; afterwards, we will look for additional attributes and actions of the sons of the enemy in other Scriptures.

According to verse 4, what else does the person who practices sin do?

___

What does the person who is of the devil practice, according to verse 8?

___

Why doesn't a believer of God practice sin? (Verse 9)

___

What two things are obvious about the children of the devil? (Verse 10)

___

Who is given as an example of the evil one in verse 12?

___

What is the person who hates his brother called in verse 15?

_____

The Devil's Family throughout Scripture

What do you learn about the Devil in 1 Peter 5:8? _____

According to Acts 13:10, what is true of the Devil? _____

According to Luke 11:18, is Satan's family united? _____

Who are the children of the Devil worshipping in Matthew 4:9-10? _____

Ultimately, who bows to whom as shown in Job 1:7? _____

Children of God, rejoice! Our Father is the Alpha and the Omega, the One who is and was and is to come, THE ALMIGHTY. Do you see the reasoning behind His declaration of THE Almighty? There is none, no not one who can frustrate, defeat or destroy our heavenly Father. Go to Him in prayer, rejoicing all the way!

A.C.T.S. PRAYER TIME

"Therefore God has highly exalted him and bestowed on him the name that is above every name, so that at the name of Jesus every knee should bow, in heaven and on earth and under the earth, and every tongue confess that Jesus Christ is Lord, to the glory of God the Father."
~ Philippians 2:9-11 ESV ~

A - Adoration_____

C - Confession_____

T - Thanksgiving_____

S - Supplication_____

DIGGING DEEPER

Read Revelation 12 to learn about Satan's sure future.

D A Y   F I V E

ON MY KNEES:

Notoriously, the half way mark of anything is difficult. The middle of a week, partway through a race or halfway to a goal, we need a shout of encouragement or a cheer of "Carry On!" Hear the shout! Stay the course, faithful student of the Word! It is eternally profitable for you to continue day-after-day fellowship with God in His Word.

Pray. "Lord, You are strong. You are the Strongest. In my weakness I flounder and feel like giving up on various tasks or assignments that You have given me. Help me to depend on You and Your strength. You say that I can call out and You will answer. Yes, if I ask for anything in Your will, You will give it to me. I want to stay the course through Your strength today for Your glory and Yours alone. Amen."

Write. 1 John 3:11-12

Read. Turn to Genesis 4 and read verses 1-16. Yes, Genesis 4:1-16.

INVESTIGATIVE STUDY

Aerial View

Streetview chapter

Under the Rug

Apply!

INVESTIGATIVE STUDY
STREETVIEW: CHAPTER 3

Today, we are going to take a short break from the book of 1 John. If John felt it was important to go back in time to give the example of Cain to his audience, it is important for us to go back and look at the example.

Use Genesis 4:1-16 to answer the questions below.

Aerial View of Cain's Example

Who were Cain's parents? _____

Who was Cain's brother? _____

Who was the oldest? _____

What was Cain's profession? _____

What was Abel's profession? _____

STREETVIEW of Cain's Example...

How close was the family to God? _____

Did Cain know what offering the Lord expected from him? _____

Did Abel do anything to Cain? _____

What was Cain's punishment? _____

How did Cain's sin affect his fellowship with God? _____

Summarize in your own words why Cain killed Abel: _____

_____

_____

_____

_____

UNDER THE RUG View of Cain's Example (in Cross Reference Passages)...

According to Matthew 23:35 was Abel guilty of any sin against Cain? _____

Look up, read and note the additional knowledge you gain about Cain & Abel from each of the passages below:

Luke 11:49-51: _____

Hebrews 12:24: _____

Jumping back to 1 John 3:12...

Why was he called a son of the evil one? _____

What was said about Abel? _____

Final Scriptural Word Summarizing Cain's example!

Write Hebrews 11:4 on the lines below: _____
_____
_____
_____

APPLY!

We can become bitter and covetous of others' successes.

Has there been a time that you can recall that you have gotten angry at someone for something they did right? For attention someone received for doing well? Do you recognize the emotion that crouched (is crouching) at your heart's door?

J – E – A – L – O – U – S – Y

Mentally note if there is someone that comes to your mind.

Love is not jealous according, to the Word. We know this, but how do you combat this tough emotion? According to 1 Peter 2:1-3, we have the answer. "Put off…envy" and "long for the pure milk of the word" so that "you may grow" in your salvation! By studying 1 John, you are able to learn more and battle the sins of the flesh. Close your time with the Lord asking for help and/or a hedge of protection from jealousy in your life and that you would put on an attitude of gratitude.

A.C.T.S. PRAYER TIME

"For the Lord God is a sun and shield; The Lord will give grace and glory;
No good thing will He withhold From those who walk uprightly."
~ Psalm 84:11 NKJV ~

A - *Adoration* _____

C - *Confession* _____

T - *Thanksgiving* _____

S - *Supplication* _____

DIGGING DEEPER

Find a quiet time this weekend and re-read the whole book of 1 John.

Billy Graham: Light to the Nations

By 1950, Billy's ministry had expanded so much that he, his wife, and some associates (evangelist Grady Wilson, master of ceremonies Cliff Burrows, soloist George Beverly Shea and Youth for Christ coworker George Wilson) organized the Billy Graham Evangelistic Association (BGEA). Its purpose was to help run Billy's ministry in an orderly, business-like manner.

The BGEA planned and coordinated meetings and crusades for Graham and his associate evangelists. It also owned Graham's weekly radio program, The Hour of Decision. As it expanded, the BGEA started a popular magazine, Decision, along with a division that produced evangelistic films. Many of these films featured actual footage from the Billy Graham crusades.

Let's read some of the stories of those whose lives have been touched and changed through the ministry of the BGEA. Although the stories are true, names and identifying details have been changed.

Norman: I can hardly wait to read Dr. Graham's latest book. As a San Francisco teenager, I gave my life to Christ at his big Crusade there. Today, I'm still going strong in the Lord. He has protected me through hearts attacks and strokes, and I will always love Him. May He continue to be with you, Billy.

Darlene: Billy, you've been an inspiration to me throughout my Christian life. I came to know Jesus during one of your Canadian Crusades in 1974. Today, I watch your sermons on television and in person, too. I have never for one second regretted turning my life over to my Lord and Savior, Jesus Christ. Thank you for taking His message to the world!

Pete: I accepted Jesus Christ as my Savior during a crusade at Memorial Coliseum in 1965. I played high school football there and remember the event as if it were yesterday. My knees rested on the thirty-yard line when Christ entered my life.

I'm so grateful to Billy for sharing Christ with me. Now nearly sixty, I was sixteen at the time I got saved and have been serving the Lord ever since. Following Christ was the most important decision I ever made. God bless you, Billy, for touching my life.

Renee: I was a privileged teenager who grew up in Sacramento, California. In the late 1950s, I sang in the choir at the Billy Graham Crusade there and was preparing to leave as a short-term missionary in Africa.

At the same time, I had a heavy heart. I didn't know whether or not either of my parents had a genuine relationship with the Lord. I found myself praying for them constantly.

Several years later, while serving in Africa, I wrote my parents to ask if they knew Christ. I was amazed at the answer. Without my realizing it, my parents had attended the Crusade when I sang in the choir. They had both gone forward to receive Christ at Dr. Graham's invitation.

Thank you, Billy Graham, for proclaiming the message of salvation in such a clear manner. Because of you, I'll see my parents in heaven one day.

Clifford: Dr. Billy Graham and his ministry have changed my life. In the early 1980s, I was involved in a religious cult. But I watched a Billy Graham crusade on television and was born again. I thank God for using Dr. Graham to bring me out of the darkness and into the light of His love.

Susan: I had always been a religious person, someone who attended church all my life. But inside, I was empty.

I went with my church group to Explo '72 in Dallas, Texas. Bill Bright and Billy Graham shared the gospel with us, and I remember coming forward to confirm my faith. After that meeting and prayer, I knew with confidence that Jesus Christ had come into my heart as my Lord and Savior.

I praise God for Billy Graham. He stepped across denominational lines to proclaim the truth. He has brought unity to the body of Christ and is a model for every minister who shares the gospel today. He leads his ministry with purity of heart and integrity, both of which are rare these days. He is the kind of righteous man Scripture praises, for his righteousness comes from God. May the Lord bless you, Billy Graham!

Johnny: I grew up in Charleston, South Carolina, and I can hardly remember a Sunday morning or evening that our family wasn't worshiping at our local church.

I was the youngest of four children. Since my siblings participated in all sorts of church activities, I did, too: Vacation Bible School, retreats, youth choir and retreats throughout the year. I had a happy childhood and was a "good boy." I knew a lot about the Bible, but I had never made a public decision for Christ.

But in 1968, when I was fourteen years old, our church youth group went to see a BGEA movie called *For Pete's Sake*. Through watching the movie, I realized I could never be "good." Through the movie, I heard and responded to a Billy Graham invitation to accept Christ. I wrote the date on the back of my ticket stub with a reminder of my decision. Although I grew up in the Church, God used a man named Billy Graham and his World Wide Pictures to save my soul for eternity.

Praise God for how He used this faithful servant in so many lives around the world! Billy Graham is mostly retired at 94 years of age, now, but the BGEA continues to influence countless lives for Christ.

DAY ONE

ON MY KNEES:

I hope you had an excellent weekend filled with a refreshing service in the Word, worshipful praise and fellowship with your local family of God. As you begin your personal time with the Lord, start in humble adoration to the Lord.

Pray. "Lord, You promise blessings to Your children who delight in your Word and meditate on it daily. I want to be like a tree planted by the water, that bears fruit and prospers. Keep me walking in Your counsel. Encourage me through the words of 1 John."

Write. Open the "My Copy of 1 John" pages in the back of your Sword Study and write 1 John 3:13-15.

Read. Do you have access to www.BibleGateway.com? If so, use the site's listen feature and follow along in your Bible as it reads 1 John Chapter 3.

INVESTIGATIVE STUDY

Apply!

INVESTIGATIVE STUDY
UNDER THE RUG:
WORD STUDY - "RIGHTEOUS"

After reading through Chapter 3 a total of six times over the last week, do you have an opinion on the Key Words that you want to investigate further?

We have chosen *righteous* and *righteousness*. If you picked a different word(s), plan to grab a Strong's or log onto Great Treasures and enjoy a rabbit trail or two as your own DIGGING DEEPER! For now, take time to look over the word study process of the word *righteous* below.

PART A: If you were to look up the word *righteous* in Strong's Concordance, you would find that the Strong's number assigned to it in 1 John is 1342. We will use this number to look up the detailed explanation of the Greek words in Part B. Below are the transliteration (the way the word is written in English), the pronunciation, and the basic definition from the Strong's lexicon (dictionary).

1342. *Righteous.* dikai□s, *dik□-ah-yos*, from 1349; equitable (in character or act); by impl. innocent, holy (absol. or rel.): - just, meet, right (-eous).

PART B: If you look up the number **1342** in another Greek lexicon, you can discover further explanations of the meaning of *righteous* in Greek as seen here:

1)   right, just, fulfilling all claims which are right and becoming.

      a.   When used in the neutral form, *dikaios* means that which is right. Whatever is listed becomes the expected way of behavior. God is the creator of the rules and regulations that man must live by in order to be deemed righteous.

      b.   When *dikaios* is used in the masculine or feminine adjective of a person, it is describing the person who acts in conformity to the God-set rules and regulations as to what are right.

      c.   When these rules and regulations are followed without failure the reference is only to God. (For example, 1 John 1:9)

PART C: We are going to hold off on Part C until we look at the word study of *righteousness* on Day 3 of this week. The two words are often used together and we want to compare the uses in 1 John.

"In the New Testament those that are called righteous (*dikaioi*) are those who conditioned their lives by the standard which is not theirs, but God's." A great example is Romans 2:13, when it states that hearers of the law are not just before God, the doers of the law will be justified. According to 2 Timothy 1:9, we are called to this "holy" calling or life. Armed with your new and deeper understanding of what it means to be *righteous*, work through the additional passages and corresponding question.

Turn to Matthew 5:43-45 (note: KJV uses "just" for 1343 in verse 45) and answer the questions below:

What is man's rule? _____

What is God's rule? _____

What is expected of the children of God? _____

How does the use of *righteous* in Matthew 23:34-35 deepen your understanding of Abel's blood?
_____

According to Matthew 25:35-40, what are some of "God's expected ways of behavior" for the *righteous* man? _____
_____

How is *righteous* described in Luke 1:6? _____

What are some of the attributes of Simeon, whom the Word describes as *righteous* (the word "just" in KJV) in Luke 2:25? _____

_____

How are the *righteous* to live, according to Romans 1:17? _____

Note all that you learn about the *righteous* in 1 Peter 3:8-12 on the lines below: _____

_____

_____

_____

Can people pretend to be *righteous*? Look up Matthew 23:27-28 and summarize what you learn about appearing *righteous*: _____

_____

A.C.T.S. PRAYER TIME

"Behold, I am the LORD, the God of all flesh: is there anything too hard for me?"
~ Jeremiah 32:27 KJV ~

A - Adoration_____

C - Confession_____

T - Thanksgiving_____

S - Supplication_____

D A Y   T W O

ON MY KNEES:

Often we can find ourselves more concerned about looking "right" before man than before our God. As we continue our research on righteousness, let's humble ourselves in prayer before the Most Righteous of all.

Pray. "Righteous God, full of wisdom, You are just and good all the time. What an immense privilege and humbling realization it is to be called a child of God. Reveal more wisdom to me as I study the Scriptures about being righteous. My heart's desire is to practice righteousness and I know I can only do that through Your Holy Spirit. Show me how today. Amen."

Write. When you write 1 John 3:16-18 today, hear the depth of God's love for you and, in turn, the depth of love you should show towards your fellow believers in Christ.

Read. Read 1 John 3 from start to finish.

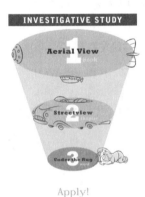

INVESTIGATIVE STUDY

Apply!

INVESTIGATIVE STUDY
UNDER THE RUG:
WORD STUDY - "RIGHTEOUSNESS"

"You know, I am pretty good." "I haven't murdered anyone." "I haven't stolen anything big." "Really, compared to so-and-so, I am nearly perfect." Ooh, how easy it can be sometimes to compare ourselves to one another. Let's look at the Greek word that John used for **righteousness** to see where we should be looking for comparisons.

PART A: If you were to look up the word **righteousness** in Strong's Concordance, you would find that the Strong's number assigned to it in 1 John 3:7 is 1343. We will use this number to look up the detailed explanation of the Greek words in Part B. Below is the transliteration, the pronunciation, and the basic definition from the Strong's lexicon.

1343. *Righteousness.* dikai☐sunē, *dik-ah-yos-ool-nay*, from 1342; equity (of character or act); spec. (Chr.) justification: - righteousness.

PART B: If you look up the number **1343** in another Greek lexicon, you can discover further explanations of the meaning of *righteousness* in Greek as seen here:

1)   Conformity or regard to God and His divine law.
2)   Opposition to lawlessness
3)   The deeds or doing of right or truth

PART C: In direct opposition to the Gnostic thought of knowledge as the end-all of man, John asserted that the mere intellectual possession of truth was not enough. ***Righteousness***, therefore, was knowing God's right ways and living them out. Interestingly, the same false sense of security exists today. Many say they believe and know God, yet their lives do not show them living in the ways of the Lord.

Watch how the insight from the definitions helps 1 John 3:7 become clearer as we replace the words ***righteous*** and ***righteousness*** with their respective definitions:

'Little children, let no man deceive you; he that doeth (righteousness) ***the deeds of truth*** is (righteous) ***right***, even as He (Jesus) is (righteous) ***right.***

The ***righteous*** are busy doing what is right. They are busy at ***righteousness***! The passages below give an example of doing ***right***…or the opposite of doing what is ***right***. Note what the ***righteous*** should be doing on the line after the reference. If the example is what not to do, then write the opposite behavior.

1 John 1:6 _____

1 John 2:4 _____

1 John 2:21 _____

1 John 3:12 _____

1 John 3:18-19 _____

After looking at the word study and John's use in 1 John, we come to the conclusion that we should be looking in the mirror and desiring to see a reflection of God's standard of ***right-eousness***. Tomorrow, we will gain further understanding and encouragement from other cross references of the word ***righteous***.

APPLY!

Just as 1 John 3:18 tells us to love in deed and truth, is there someone with whom you can share the Good News in word or action? Pray that God would bring someone to your mind to whom you can be an example of His love in how you talk or live. Write his or her name here, pray for him or her and be ready to share the Good News of Jesus if you are asked about why you live the way you do.

My friend's name: _____

A.C.T.S. PRAYER TIME

"For I know that in me (that is, in my flesh,) dwelleth no good thing: for to will is present with me;
but how to perform that which is good I find not."
~ Romans 7:18 KJV ~

A - *Adoration*_____

C - *Confession*_____

T - *Thanksgiving*_____

S - *Supplication*_____

D A Y   T H R E E

ON MY KNEES:

We are God's little children if we have believed in Jesus' name. Remembering that we are not in control, but that our God is sovereignly caring for us is such a great comfort. Bow before Him in prayer before we go to His feet through the study of His Word.

Pray. "Father, yes, Heavenly Father, I am so blessed to be one of Your children. I know that through Your Word, You assure me that I am one of Your own. As I love in deed and truth, continue to give me confidence in Your love. I am looking forward to hearing from You through John's words today. Help me understand Your holy character in greater depth. Amen."

Write. Write 1 John 3:19-20 on the next lines of your "My Copy of 1 John" pages.

Read. Read 1 John 3 aloud.

INVESTIGATIVE STUDY

Aerial View

Streetview

Under the Rug

Apply!

INVESTIGATIVE STUDY
UNDER THE RUG:
CROSS REFERENCES - "RIGHTEOUS"

Today, we are going to take a slight turn from our normal cross reference process. While we will be looking at various Scriptures containing the word *righteous*, we will be more concerned about the lifestyle and story of those the Lord called *righteous*. We can learn from their examples since God considered their behavior *righteous*. We will give you a passage. You will note the name of the example of the *righteous* man and then summarize his life. Finally, you will note your greatest "take away" from his life to apply to yours. If you are using the King James Version, the word "just" is sometimes used for *righteous*.

For example, if you read a passage that said, "My mom wakes at six o'clock every morning to spend time in prayer, study of God's Word and memorizing Bible passages." You might fill the blanks like this:

When I grow up I want to be like "my mom" by: "diligently drawing near to the Lord each morning."

Genesis 6:5-9

Person: _____

Summary: _____

_____

_____

I want to be like "_____" by: _____

Proverbs 9:9

Person: _____

Summary: _____

_____

_____

I want to be like "_____" by: _____

Proverbs 10:31-32

Person: _____

Summary: _____

_____

_____

I want to be like "_____" by: _____

Proverbs 20:7

Person: _____

Summary: _____

_____

_____

I want to be like "_____" by: _____

Matthew 1:19

Person: _____

Summary: _____

_____

_____

I want to be like "_____" by: _____

Mark 6:20

Person: _____

Summary: _____

_____

_____

I want to be like "_____" by: _____

Luke 2:25-28

Person: _____

Summary: _____

_____

_____

I want to be like "_____" by: _____

Luke 23:50-53

Person: _____

Summary: _____

_____

_____

I want to be like "_____" by: _____

Acts 10:22-33

Person: _____

Summary: _____

_____

_____

I want to be like "_____" by: _____

2 Peter 2:6-8

Person: _____

Summary: _____

_____

_____

I want to be like "_____" by: _____

Use your prayer time to call on the Lord for strength in walking in *righteousness* like the earthly example above who most encouraged you.

A.C.T.S. PRAYER TIME

A - *Adoration* _____

C - *Confession* _____

T - *Thanksgiving* _____

S - *Supplication* _____

DAY FOUR

ON MY KNEES:

How good it is to know we are a part of the Body of Christ and not alone in learning to walk in His ways. Hearing the encouragement of men and women who were like us with their faults and battles helps us to carry on in the walks that the Lord has given us. Before we continue in our study of 1 John, pause in prayer.

Pray. "Oh, yes, Lord…You are God and there is no other like YOU! May Your purposes, which were and are established long before my lifetime, be accomplished in Your good pleasure in my life through studying Your Word. May I witness Your hand bringing Your will to pass to accomplish the greatest glory in my life. In Jesus' name, I pray." (Isaiah 46:9-11)

Write. 1 John 3:21-24 in your copy of 1 John.

Read. Once again, with a cheerful attitude, read 1 John 3 aloud to yourself.

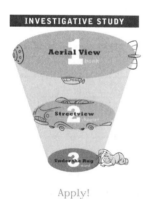

Apply!

INVESTIGATIVE STUDY
UNDER THE RUG:
CROSS REFERENCES -
"RIGHTEOUSNESS" AND "RIGHTEOUS"

There is, of course, a better example of a ***righteous*** man than all those that we investigated yesterday. He stands far above all others. We have reserved today for Him, and Him alone.

Jesus became flesh, first and foremost, for our salvation, but He also came to show us how to walk in a manner that was pleasing to His Father. He was the perfect example of ***righteousness*** and being ***righteous***!

Following the same pattern as we did yesterday, look up the passages below and fill in the blanks. Although, this time, instead of writing the person's name, note the characteristic that Jesus displayed in the passage. Charge!

Matthew 5:6-13

Person: _____

Summary: _____

_____

_____

I want to be like "Jesus" by: _____

Matthew 9:10-13

Person: _____

Summary: _____

_____

_____

I want to be like "Jesus" by: _____

Matthew 12:49-50

Person: _____

Summary: _____

_____

_____

I want to be like "Jesus" by: _____

Matthew 20:26-28

Person: _____

Summary: _____

_____

_____

I want to be like "Jesus" by: _____

Mark 6:34

Person: _____

Summary: _____

_____

_____

I want to be like "Jesus" by: _____

Mark 10:13-14

Person: _____

Summary: _____

_____

_____

I want to be like "Jesus" by: _____

Romans 6:11-13

Person: _____

Summary: _____

_____

_____

I want to be like "Jesus" by: _____

Ephesians 4:32

Person: _____

Summary: _____

_____

_____

I want to be like "Jesus" by: _____

Philippians 2:12-18

Person: _____

Summary: _____

_____

_____

I want to be like "Jesus" by: _____

Colossians 3:12-14

Person: _____

Summary: _____

_____

_____

I want to be like "Jesus" by: _____

1 Peter 2:19-24

Person: _____

Summary: _____

_____

_____

I want to be like "Jesus" by: _____

Jesus is our Savior, Master and Brother. As you looked at His "older brother" example of *righteousness*, what characteristic do you find most difficult? Go to Him in prayer and share your desire to be more like Him.

A.C.T.S. PRAYER TIME

"Give instruction to a wise man and he will be still wiser,
Teach a righteous man and he will increase his learning."
~ Proverbs 9:9 NASB ~

A - Adoration_____

C - Confession_____

T - Thanksgiving_____

S - Supplication_____

"I have one desire now - to live a life of reckless abandon for the Lord,
putting all my energy and strength into it."
~ Elisabeth Elliot ~

DIGGING DEEPER

Why should we follow Jesus' example? Look up, read and then summarize what you learn in the passages below.

John 13:14-15 _____
_____

Philippians 2:4-11 _____
_____

Hebrews 12:1-6 _____
_____

D A Y   F I V E

O N M Y K N E E S :

We are here! The end of another week and another Day 10 Diagram! Completing the diagrams for each chapter of 1 John will give you a great summary page that will remind you for many years to come of all that the Lord has taught you in this short letter of encouragement and confidence. Before we begin coloring and documenting, take a few minutes to prepare your heart and ask for an attentive heart to the last summary lessons the Lord may have for you in 1 John 3.

Pray. "Yes, Lord, yes! You have reminded me many, many times – who can frustrate YOU? Not a single soul, no, not one. I know that You will work in, through and around me in the highest of ways. Help me see Your hand moving and continue to use me as You see fit whether "as I am" – in new ways – or in different ways – just may it be YOUR way! I want to be known to You as a doer, not a just a talker. I do not want to pretend before others, I want to wholeheartedly please You as I walk in Your ways." (Isaiah 14: 27)

Write. Look over your handwritten copy of 1 John 3. Have you marked all the references to God? Have you noted what you have learned in the left margin under each person of the Trinity?

Read. As you finish up the detailed investigation of Chapter 3, read all of 1 John today before moving to your Day 10 Diagram.

INVESTIGATIVE STUDY

Apply!

I N V E S T I G A T I V E S T U D Y
1-2-3 SUMMARIZE: CHAPTER 3

We have arrived at another "Day 10 Diagram" summary! Take a quick look back at the first two Diagrams. Think about the summaries of the first two chapters of 1 John. Now, complete your Diagram for 1 John 3.

☐ To begin, look at the top of the day 10 Diagram. Fill in the chapter number. Look at Week 1, Day 5 for the original title you created for 1 John 3. Review what you wrote and refine your title with the new insights that you have learned over the last 10 days.

☐ Next, which verse from the chapter do you think was the "key verse?"

☐ On the right of the page, transfer your key Greek words from this chapter. Write the English words on the top line after the words "Greek Words." Transfer the Greek spellings and write a short definition of their meanings.

☐ On the bottom of the Diagram page, transfer the most important things that you learned about God through marking the references about Him on your "Write!" pages.

In Chapter 3 of his letter, John continues to highlight the contrast between living in God's light and living in darkness.   Our fellow believers in the Day 10 Diagram have chosen to "walk in the light as God is in the light."   On the line above the lighthouse, label their side of the chasm, "Light."   Fill in the blanks on the lighthouse with your favorite attributes of God that were mentioned in 1 John 3. "Darkness" is an apt title for the opposite side of the chasm, where those opposed to God abide. Put that word on the line within the clouds.

In 1 John 3, John has taught the Christian recipients (and us!) about the differences between the children of God and the children of the devil. On the first blank under the lighthouse, write, "Children of God" and list three things John says about these beloved, adopted children of God's family. The three descriptions of the "Children of the devil" (write that title on the top blank on the opposite side of the page) are very different- list what John shared about this other group in Chapter 3.

The magnificent cross is the only bridge across the eternally deep chasm, and highlights the heart of God- indeed, as John proclaims, "God is _____." (Fill in the missing word on your diagram.) Color the heart on the cross red and write a passage reference that is your favorite description of God's love for you.

On which side have you chosen to abide?

A.C.T.S. PRAYER TIME

"See what kind of love the Father has given to us, that we should be called children of God; and so we are. The reason why the world does not know us is that it did not know him."
~ 1 John 3:1 ESV ~

A - *Adoration* _____

C - *Confession* _____

T - *Thanksgiving* _____

S - *Supplication* _____

Title: _____

Chapter: _____

Key Verse: _____

Greek Words: _____

Corrie ten Boom: Light in a Dark Era

Corrie ten Boom, a watchmaker by trade, was imprisoned by the Nazis on February 28, 1944 for assisting Jews in her native Holland. She and other family members endured horrible conditions and terrible treatment. After her release, Corrie never stopped proclaiming the gospel of Christ and the message of forgiveness. In this series of fictional letters (based on true events) shared from the concentration camp, she tells part of her story.

March 3, 1944

My dear friends,

I have no idea if you will receive these writings or not. I will keep them short so as to avoid the guards' prying eyes. But in a day when lies have overtaken our precious Holland, I want to speak the truth. And I want to continue to share the deep love of my Father in heaven.

These may well be the only love letters I will ever write.

My family has a long history of service to our God and His people. My great-grandfather Willem, a watchmaker like me, owned the clock shop he passed down to my father, Casper ten Boom. Willem loved God's holy people and held meetings to "pray for the peace of Jerusalem." My father held the same kind of meetings and taught us as children to love the Savior and pray for the Jewish people. What that would come to mean, only time would tell.

I can write no more now. I send this with deep love and affection, your sister,

-Corrie

April 14, 1944

Beloved of the Lord,

And so you are. He loves you with an everlasting love, and His love under-lies all earthly loves.

How did we come here? I will tell you a little more. Our family never stopped caring for the Jews. We studied their language. We celebrated their feasts. They knew us always as their friends.

Times grew hard, and the Nazis worked to destroy God's people. It seemed only natural for the sons and daughters of Israel to turn to us.

First, I helped find places for them to stay in the countryside. And before long, we ten Booms were opening our home to Jews who needed refuge. I had a false wall built in my bedroom so I could hide people there. And soon, I was help-ing others hide these suffering servants as well.

What we did broke the Nazis' law. But God's law is higher. My fam-ily and I could not turn away from His people, and we trust that, even here in prison, He will never turn His back on us.

In faith,
Corrie

June 6, 1944

Dear Ones,

Since my last letter, the Nazis have sent us to another prison where they have brought many more of my fellow Hollanders. I do not know whether or not they, like my family, were aiding Jews.

We have little time to talk without someone listening. And when we do, my sister Betsie (whom I now see at times) and I try to share the knowledge of God. Knowing Him is the only way to true love and abundant life—even in prison. From our earliest days, our parents passed down this truth.

Papa, like Jesus, often taught through story. As a young girl, I feared the death of one or more family members. Many of them suffered from poor health. But my Papa asked me, "When we take the train to Amsterdam, when do I give you the ticket?"

"Just before we get on the train."

"And so God will give you the courage to carry the pain when the time comes for someone to die. Until then you should not carry it."

Papa's wisdom helps Betsie and me as we live for the Lord here behind the prison walls. And it helps us shoulder the pain of his passing. We have learned he died only ten days after imprisonment.

I must go before a guard finds me writing. I will share more at another time.

Trusting Him,
Corrie

July 12, 1944

Dear Friends,

And how did we come here, you ask? Did the guards find Jews hidden in our household? Did one of our number break down and reveal our many actions on behalf of God's chosen people?

No. What happened proved much more painful. A man came into the shop and said he and his wife had been hiding Jews. The police had taken her to jail, and he needed money to bribe an officer. I had little but gave him what I had.

A few short hours later, the Nazis came to our home to arrest us. This man was no partner in our work. He had betrayed us. In all, thirty-five people were arrested that day. My one consolation: the six Jews tucked into the hiding place in my bedroom remained free.

God cared for them. And He cares for us here in this prison.

I will tell more of the story as He grants me the time and freedom.

With gratitude,

Corrie

Learn more about God's powerful provision for Corrie and her
fellow prisoners next week!

D A Y   O N E

ON MY KNEES:

We are starting a new chapter of 1 John today! What a privilege it is to continue to mature in the understanding of the Word of God. Continue faithfully in the hard work of deeply investigating the Scriptures! Start again with prayer.

Pray. "You are God, the One who sits above the earth, Who stretched out the heavens like a curtain. You have no equal. While I am like a grasshopper, You do not grow weary or tired. You give me strength and increase my power when I call for help in my weakness and weariness. Do it again, Lord - strengthen me, please. Amen."

Write. Turn to a new page in the "Write!" portion of your Sword Study and write 1 John 4:1.

Read. Turn from your well-read pages of Chapter 3 to Chapter 4 and read all 21 verses before beginning your study. Be sure to have your red colored pencil handy for marking all of the occurrences of the word "love".

Apply!

INVESTIGATIVE STUDY
STREETVIEW: CHAPTER 4

Whew! 1 John 4 is definitely characterized by John's repetitive style. This week we will slow down the spinning carousal by breaking down the chapter through the interview process. We will ask the "Why," "How" and "What" questions until we have a clearer understanding of all that John is sharing with us.   Let's get started!

Us and Them – How to Know

Chapter 4, verses 1-8

According to 1 John 4:1, should we trust everyone who says they have wisdom from God? _____

Why or why not? _____

_____

How can we know if someone has the Spirit of God, according to verse 2? _____

_____

How can we know if someone has the spirit of the anitichrist, according to verse 3? _____

_____

According to verse 4, whose spirit is greater? _____

What three things do we learn about the antichrist in verse 5? _____
_____

In verse 6, what two spirits are described?

Spirit of _____ and spirit of _____

In verse 7, we are given a command; what is it? _____

What is the reasoning behind the command? _____

Also in verse 7, what two things do we hear are true of those who love? _____
_____

Using verse 8, finish this sentence: God is... _____

APPLY!

Go to a local, public place such as a coffee shop, mall or public transportation stop. With your parents' permission, ask 20-25 strangers if you can ask them two questions. Ask them the questions in the chart below. Tally their responses under the "Yes" or "No" column. If they offer you a reason why they answered the way they did, note their comment in the "Why" column.

QUESTION	YES	NO	COMMENT (WHY?)
Do you believe Jesus came to earth from heaven?			
Do you believe Jesus is God's Son?			

A.C.T.S. PRAYER TIME

A - Adoration_____

C - Confession_____

T - Thanksgiving_____

S - Supplication_____

D A Y   T W O

ON MY KNEES:

Are you on top of your game or under the weather? Either way, share your innermost feelings with the Lord openly. He is able to handle each one of our emotions. Go speak with Him through prayer.

Pray. "Father, You alone hear my thoughts, cries and feelings with unbiased ears and eternal patience. I want to deepen my relationship with You. Permanently impress Your words on my heart so that I would leave my time greatly affected."

Write. Turn to your "Write!" section and write 1 John 4:2-3.

Read. Before beginning your INVESTIGATIVE STUDY, read Chapter 4 of 1 John.

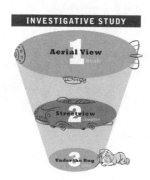

Apply!

INVESTIGATIVE STUDY
STREETVIEW: CHAPTER 4

Yesterday, we questioned the first six verses of 1 John 4. Today, we will look at the same six verses in light of other Scripture passages. In order to gain more insight, we will take apart the verses, phrase by phrase, and see how the non-1 John verse uses the same phrase or word.

Read the 1 John 4 verse, then turn to the listed passage. Summarize how the new verses support or deepen the words of 1 John on the lines provided.

Verse 1: "Many false prophets…" see 2 Peter 2:1.
Summary: _____
_____

Verse 2: "Knowing the Spirit of God…" see 1 Corinthians 12:3.
Summary: _____
_____

Verse 3: "The spirit that does not confess…" see 2 John 7.
Summary: _____
_____

Verse 4: "Greater is He…" see Romans 8:31-39

Summary: _____

_____

"Greater is He…" see John 14:25-27

Summary: _____

_____

Verse 5: "They are from the world…" see John 15:19

Summary: _____

_____

"They are from the world..." See John 17:14

Summary: _____

_____

Verse 6: "Who listens to God…" see John 10:3-4

Summary:_____

_____

Verse 7: "Knows God…" see 1 Corinthians 8:3

Summary: _____

_____

Verse 8: "God is love…" see Romans 8:39

Summary: _____

_____

A . C . T . S . P R A Y E R T I M E

"For my brothers and companions' sake I will say, 'Peace be within you!'
For the sake of the house of the Lord our God, I will seek your good."
~ Psalm 122:8-9 ESV ~

A - *Adoration* _____

C - *Confession* _____

T - *Thanksgiving* _____

S - *Supplication* _____

DIGGING DEEPER

1 John 4:3 describes the spirit of the antichrist as "every spirit who does not confess Jesus as Christ." "Anti" means against. Find each of the passages below. Read them carefully and summarize what additional information they give you on the antichrists.

1 John 2:18 _____

1 John 2:22 _____

2 John 7 _____

Matthew 24:5 _____

Matthew 24:24 _____

D A Y   T H R E E

ON MY KNEES:

Greetings! Do you come in anticipation? Are you somewhat distracted by what you have planned for later today? Either way, go to Him for a time of sweet fellowship in prayer.

Pray. "Oh, Lord, I do not want You to be like the little things on my list. I do not want to consider our time together as just a good project or goal to accomplish. I know it must sadden You when I long for other "stuff" or the things of the world more than You. Help me to want nothing more than my desire to meet with You. Change me and deepen my longing for You so that it supersedes any of my other desires.

Write. 1 John 4:4-5 on the next lines of your "Write" section.

Read. Once again, please read Chapter 4 of 1 John.

INVESTIGATIVE STUDY
STREETVIEW: *CHAPTER 4*

INVESTIGATIVE STUDY

1 **Aerial View**

2 **Streetview**

3 **Under the Rug**

Apply!

It's time to finish questioning the remaining verses of 1 John, Chapter 4. Repetitive investigation from different angles allows us to thoroughly understand these passages. So, carry on!

1 John 4, Verses 9-11:

What has God done because of His love? _____

Why was Jesus sent into the world? _____

Why should we love one another? _____

Verses 12-16:

Has God ever been seen? _____

What two things happen if we love one another? _____
_____

What are we given if we are one of God's children, according to verse 13? _____

Why did the Father send the Son? _____

What happens if we confess that Jesus is God's Son? _____

Finish the sentence: God is... _____

Verses 17-21:

How can we approach the Day of Judgment? _____

What four things do we learn about fear in verse 18?

_____

_____

_____

_____

Why do we love God? _____

Why do we love people? _____

According to verse 20, what makes a person a liar? _____

Write the commandment of verse 21 in your own words on the line below: _____

_____

As we wrap up the questioning of Chapter 4, let's review John's exhortations. Write out the exhortations after each of the listed references.

1 John 4:1 _____

1 John 4:7 _____

1 John 4:11 _____

1 John 4:21 _____

A.C.T.S. PRAYER TIME

"And I said: 'I pray, Lord God of heaven, O great and awesome God, You who keep Your covenant and mercy with those who love You and observe Your commandments,'"
~ Nehemiah 1:5 NKJV~

A - *Adoration* _____

C - *Confession* _____

T - *Thanksgiving* _____

S - *Supplication* _____

D A Y   F O U R

ON MY KNEES:

Often right after we exclaim, "Yes, we win!," a "snoopy dance" occurs...and then, a losing round. Just when we feel as though we have things under control or are doing such a great job of walking well, we can come crashing down. The Lord calls us to come to His Word for a daily meal. His wisdom understands our need for His direction on a regular basis, not every once in a while. You are faithfully seeking Him by being in His Word. Carry on, diligent child of God!

Pray. Indeed, Lord...You always succeed. Where we fail, when we are fearful, faithless, faulty – sinful- You hit the mark dead center. I praise You this morning for the great and mighty things that Your Word does...not a single, empty word proceeds from Your mouth. Thank You, Lord, for washing us with Your words. Thank You for leaving us with Your Word so that we might be strengthened, cleansed, established, perfected, and comforted by it. (Isaiah 55:11)

Write. Neatly write the next three verses in 1 John 4 (verses 6-8).

Read. Once again, read 1 John 4.

INVESTIGATIVE STUDY
STREETVIEW: CHAPTER 4

INVESTIGATIVE STUDY

Aerial View 1

Streetview 2

Under the Rug 3

Apply!

Have you guessed what we are going to do today? You got it! We will revisit verses 9 through 21 by looking at similar phrases elsewhere in Scripture.

Verse 10: "He loves us..." see Romans 5:8

Summary: _____

_____

_____

Verse 12: "No one has seen God...." see 1 Timothy 6:16

Summary: _____

_____

Verse 14: "Father has sent the Son..." see John 3:17

Summary: _____

_____

Verse 15: "Whoever confesses…" see Romans 10:9-10

Summary: _____

_____

Verse 21: "This commandment we have…" see Leviticus 19:18

Summary: _____

_____

"This commandment we have…" see John 13:34

Summary: _____

_____

"This commandment we have..." see Matthew 22:37-39

What is the first commandment? _____

What is the second commandment? _____

Finish your time with the Lord using Matthew 22:37-39 as a foundation for your closing prayer.

A . C . T . S .   P R A Y E R   T I M E

"Jesus said unto him, 'Thou shalt love the Lord thy God with all thy heart, and with all thy soul, and with all thy mind. This is the first and great commandment.'"
~ Matthew 22:37-38 KJV ~

A - *Adoration* _____

C - *Confession* _____

T - *Thanksgiving* _____

S - *Supplication* _____

D A Y   F I V E

ON MY KNEES:

As you join the Lord in His Word each day, you offer your time and life as a sacrifice to Him. There are many options and alternative ways to spend the next 30 minutes. Praise the Lord that His Spirit has drawn you close through His Word!

Pray. "Lord, You give me light and truth in Your Word, so let them lead me to Your holy hill and dwelling place. When my soul is down or in turmoil, turn my heart to the hope that is in Your words. You are my salvation and my God. Give me joy as we spend time together today. In Your powerful name, I pray."

Write. Grab your pen or pencil and begin to write 1 John 4:9-10 in the "Write!" section of your Sword Study.

Read. Be creative. Come up with a different approach to reading through Chapter 4 of 1 John today.

INVESTIGATIVE STUDY

1 — Aerial View

2 — Streetview chapter

3 — Under the Rug

Apply!

INVESTIGATIVE STUDY
STREETVIEW: CHAPTER 4

Take a moment to re-read 1 John 4 verses 9, 10 and 14. These verses detail the Good News. Paraphrase the words of 1 John 4:9, 10 and 14 to create a salvation message to share. Insert the specific details of your salvation day and of your continued walk in salvation.

_____

_____

_____

_____

_____

_____

_____

_____

_____

_____

_____

_____

_____

APPLY!

Share your story with someone today!

A.C.T.S. PRAYER TIME

A - *Adoration*_____

C - *Confession*_____

T - *Thanksgiving*_____

S - *Supplication*_____

DIGGING DEEPER

Find a quiet time this weekend and re-read the whole book of 1 John.

Corrie ten Boom: Light in a Dark Era
(continued)

September 18, 1944

Precious Partners,

Betsie and I remain so grateful for your prayers. We have been transferred to another prison, Ravensbruck, and see each other much more often now.

In this place, prisoners care for one another in small but large ways, sharing a thin blanket or a crust of bread.

Betsie remains herself. She serves and loves each one with God's deep love. She has that kind, tender affection Scripture encourages us to have.

I, on the other hand, am far more selfish. But I remain so grateful for our loving Lord. He has allowed us to keep a small Bible in our tiny collection of belongings.

When we entered the prison, I hid it on my back under my clothing. But I feared the guards would take it away. I said, "O Lord, send Your angels, that they surround me."

And then I thought, Yes, but angels are spirits and you can look through a spirit. So I told Him, "O God, let Your angels this time not be transparent."

And He did! The guards searched the woman in front of me. They searched my sister, right behind me. But the angels covered me, and the guards did not see me. I entered the prison with my Bible.

Praising Him,
Corrie

November 8, 1944

Dear Fellow Servants of the King,

My sister and I continue to serve from behind the prison walls. Here, we have the privilege of holding small worship services in praise of our Lord. We thank Him for the fleas because they keep the guards from entering our cell block. Our loving Father brings light into darkness—even through the fleas.

At one point, the guards gave me a vision test to see if I could perform another type of labor. I knew Betsie had no such strength. I made sure I missed most of the questions. God watched out for me, and I am now assigned to knitting duty right beside my beloved sister.

God continues to perform miracles on our behalf. Food is scarce and many, including my sweet Betsie, have grown very thin. I am sharing my old bottle of vitamins, hoping to keep up everyone's strength despite the poor rations. Every day, I think the supply will end, and every day, more vitamins remain.

He is Lord,
Corrie

December 3, 1944

Dear Saints,

Betsie grows frailer by the day. However, she still manages to serve others and encourage them in the Lord. She also takes time to share with me her vision for the future: "Sister, we will have a house again—a house that will help those damaged by these camps. We will serve both the prisoners and the guards, anyone whose life has suffered the trauma of this time in history."

Her ability to envision a life outside the camp amazes me. I have difficulty thinking beyond our daily bread. But Betsie uses her heart to see God's plan for good and not for evil, to give us a future and a hope.

Truly, my sister loves with the sacrificial love of Christ. Her willingness to pray for even our captors—who treat us with indifference at best and cruelty at worst—shows the depth of her love.

I often pray, "Lord, make me more like You." Today, could You make me a little more like Betsie, too?

In hopeful expectation,
Corrie

December 17, 1944

Our Family,

Today's news weighs heavy on my heart.

Betsie now has a life outside the camp. She stands strong and whole with our Lord in heaven.

Yesterday, when she could no longer rise for roll call, a friend and I carried her out. Later, we returned her to bed. Although those in charge had already denied permission, one guard cared enough to admit her to the hospital.

I visited at noon and found her resting. That evening, the guards would not allow me to visit. I peered through the hospital window and realized she lay dead. My sweet, caring sister no longer had to bear the pain of the camp or the concerns of others. Her face showed her peace.

And with this, I could let her go.

Trusting Him,

Corrie

Through a clerical error, Corrie ten Boom was released from Ravensbruck three days after her sister found her final freedom. She made her way back to Holland, received care in a hospital, and returned to their former home in Haarlem. Corrie began to speak out about the horrors of the concentration camps and how God had held her close.

She used every meeting as a way to share Betsie's vision for a home to help people heal from wartime trauma. She received financial gifts along with the donation of a home almost identical to the one her sister had envisioned. Its first residents were those who had been hidden away as well as those who had been imprisoned.

Corrie spent the rest of her life telling Betsie's story. Eventually, she moved to the United States. She wrote seven books, including The Hiding Place, which also became a movie. Until her death in 1983, Corrie ten Boom preached the messages of sacrificial love and forgiveness lived out by her sister Betsie. She became a true light in a dark era.

D A Y   O N E

ON MY KNEES:

Welcome to another week of allowing the Word to work in you. As you arrive to study, realize that there is such a great opportunity before you as the Lord refines you for His purposes. Before we begin our word studies, let's draw closer to the Lord in prayer.

Pray. Holy Spirit, it is You, my King, Lord, Master, Creator, that is at work in me. You are working and desire to accomplish all that is good for YOUR good pleasure. Oh, I know that is what I want in my life – Your will and not mine! Lord, do whatever You desire so that I might be refined, that we might be refined, that Your Bride might be drawn closer to You. (Philippians 2:13)

Write. Please write 1 John 4:11-13 in your copy of 1 John.

Read. Open up your Bible to 1 John and read Chapter 4.

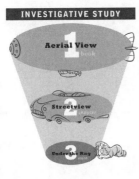

Apply!

INVESTIGATIVE STUDY
UNDER THE RUG:
WORD STUDY - "LOVE"

"Beloved." What a neat way for John to keep addressing his readers. He uses it three times in Chapter 4. Wonder if he is repeating the command to himself as well? Be-loved. *Love* one another. God is *love*. He *loved* us. *Love* is an attribute of those who know God.

There is no doubt that love is a Key Word to this chapter…and the whole book of 1 John. It has actually been difficult to hold off studying this word until now, but as we come to Chapter 4, it is time.

In your Bible, highlight each instance of the word *"love"* in 1 John using a red colored pencil. If you would prefer not to mark in your Bible, use an online resource and copy the text to a word processing document. Double space the verses while you are formatting.

Now, with lightening speed, fill in the blanks below with the reference written as chapter/verse (for example, 1 John 1:1 would be written as 1:1) then write up to four words describing what you learned about *love*. John is certainly a teacher at heart as he repeats, repeats and repeats lessons. Anyone who has taught knows that this is how we learn best as students. Evidently, this is also the teaching method that God is using as well! There are so many instances of *love* that we will do half today and half tomorrow; simply stop when you have filled half of the lines!

Chapter/Verse	...And About Love	Chapter/Verse	...And About Love
2:5	Love of God		

A.C.T.S. PRAYER TIME

"By this all men will know that you are My disciples, if you have love for one another."
~ John 13:35 NASB ~

A - Adoration_____

C - Confession_____

T - Thanksgiving_____

S - Supplication_____

"Discipleship begins when you decide to respond to Jesus' call with obedience. You are not a disciple if you are just an admirer of Jesus from a distance. You are not a disciple if you used to follow Jesus. You are not a disciple if you are not seeking to know what He said or learn how He lived. Many call themselves disciples but aren't. It's got to be complete surrender."
~ Trent Griffith ~

DAY TWO

ON MY KNEES:

Love. I love chocolate. I love this game. I love dogs. God is love. One of these things just doesn't go with the others! We need to come before the Lord today and ask for His wisdom and understanding concerning the word "love" with hopes that we will move beyond our day's overuse to His application of the Word.

Pray. "Indeed, my God…Now to You who is able to do far more abundantly beyond all that we ask or THINK, according to the power that works within us, to You be the glory. As I come before You in Your Word, teach me what You meant when You said You were love and I am to love my fellow brothers and sisters in Your family. Amen." (Ephesians 3:20-21)

Write. As you write 1 John 4:14-16, don't forget to mark all the references to God and transfer what you learn to the margin of your page.

Read. Grab your mom or dad and read Chapter 4 aloud with each other, taking turns every three verses, or so.

INVESTIGATIVE STUDY

Aerial View
1 look

Streetview
2

Under the Rug
3 word

Apply!

INVESTIGATIVE STUDY
UNDER THE RUG:
WORD STUDY - "LOVE"

Before we move to the word study of *love*, turn back a page and finish up your marking of the word within the book of 1 John.

The Greek language is much richer in words for *love* than English. In English we only have one word that is supposed to convey all of the possible meanings of *love*. Usually, context helps us: you don't *love* your mom the same way that you love pizza! Greek, on the other hand, used four different words to convey different nuances in the idea of *love*: *storgay*, *eros*, *phileo* and *agape*. We will examine them in this order.

Storgay

This word for *love* does not appear in the New Testament, but it is found inside a compound word (with *phileo*) in Romans 12:10. We also find a negative word derived from it in Romans 1:31 and 2 Timothy 3:3.

PART A: As we look up the word *kindly affectionate/devoted/love* in the Strong's Concordance, we find that the Strong's number assigned to it in Romans 12:10 is 5387. Note this, because it will be used to look up a detailed explanation of the Greek word in Part B. Below is the transliteration (which is how we write the word in the English language), the pronunciation, and then the basic definition from the Strong's lexicon.

>   **5387.** philostorgos, *fil-os'-tor-gos*, from 5384 and storge (cherishing one's kindred, especially parents or children); fond of natural relatives, i.e. fraternal
>   towards fellow Christian:--kindly affectioned.

PART B: We will now look up the number 5387 in another Greek lexicon to discover a more detailed explanation of the word *kindly affectionate/devoted/love* in Greek:
   1) the mutual love of parents and children and wives and husbands
   2) loving affection, prone to love, loving tenderly
   >   a) chiefly of the reciprocal tenderness of parents and children

Eros

PART A: Eros also does not appear in the New Testament (though the name Erastus in Acts 19:22, Romans 16:23, and 1 Timothy 4:20 comes from the verb erao). Therefore, we won't find a Strong's number attached to it. But the transliteration (the way we write the word in English) and basic definition can be found below. We generally might think of this kind of love as the romantic/sexual love between a husband and a wife.
   Eros 1. love, desire, Hom., etc. 2. as nom. pr. Eros, the god of love, Hes.

Phileo

PART A: As we look up this word for *love* in the Strong's Concordance, we find that the Strong's number assigned to it in John 21:17 is 5368. Note this, because it will be used to look up a detailed explanation of the Greek word in Part B.

Below is the transliteration , the pronunciation, and then the basic definition from the Strong's lexicon.

>   **5368.** phileo, *fil-eh'-o*, from 5384; to be a friend to (fond of [an individual or an object]),
>   i.e. have affection for--kiss, love.

PART B: We will now look up the number 5368 in another Greek lexicon to discover a more detailed explanation of the Greek word *phileo*:
   1) to love
   >   a) to approve of
   >   b) to like
   >   c) sanction
   >   d) to treat affectionately or kindly, to welcome, befriend
   2) to show signs of love
   >   a) to kiss
   3) to be fond of doing
   >   a) be wont, use to do

Agape

PART A: As we look up the word *charity/love[ing]* in the Strong's Concordance, we find that the Strong's number assigned to it in 1 Peter 4:8 is 26. Note this, because it will be used to look up a detailed explanation of the Greek word in Part B. Below is the transliteration (which is how we write the word in the English language), the pronunciation, and then the basic definition from the Strong's lexicon.

26. <u>agape.</u> *ag-ah'-pay*; from 25; love, i.e. affection or benevolence; specially (plur.) a love-feast:--(feast of) charity (-ably), dear, love.

PART B: We will now look up the number 26 in another Greek lexicon to discover a more detailed explanation of the word charity/love[ing] in Greek:

1) Affection, good will, love, benevolence, brotherly love.

2) Benevolent. This type of love is shown by the "lover" giving "loved" what they **need** versus what they may **want.**

3) Unconditional, self sacrificing.

PART C: The Strong's definition says that the main difference between the last two Greek words for *love* is that *agapao* (verb form of *agape*) is a matter of the head, and *phileo* is a matter of the heart. Or we might say that *agapao* is a decision to love, whereas *phileo* is the affection involved.

A.C.T.S. PRAYER TIME

"So now faith, hope, and love abide, these three; but the greatest of these is love."
~ 1 Corinthians 13:13 ESV ~

A - Adoration_____

C - Confession_____

T - Thanksgiving_____

S - Supplication_____

"Disciples are called to a radical, growing relationship with Jesus. Disciples are called to die to self in order that they may live. Disciples are called to give so they can keep. It is a call to put others first and themselves last. Disciples will be required to speak up when others remain quiet. Disciples are prompted to move in directions with no known destinations."
~ Trent Griffith ~

D A Y   T H R E E

ON MY KNEES:

Welcome to the middle of the week, everything is downhill from here! Is that really true? Whether you are sailing smoothly through this week or struggling through every minute of the each day, realize that there is nothing too difficult for the Lord. Everything can be too difficult for us. We need to lean on His strength. Let's go before His throne in prayer.

Pray. "According to Genesis 18:14, there is nothing too difficult for You, Lord! In Your name, I pray for the floodgates to be open. May I be prompted by Your Spirit to respond and act in ways that reflect Your Spirit within me. Let me rest in Your ways and know that You do all things in their appointed times. In Your Almighty name, I pray. Amen."

Write. Prayerfully write 1 John 4:17-19. Ponder your confidence as you write. In whom is your trust?

Read. Before you begin your Greek word study, please read Chapter 4 of 1 John.

INVESTIGATIVE STUDY
UNDER THE RUG:
CROSS REFERENCES - "LOVE"

INVESTIGATIVE STUDY

Aerial View
1

Streetview
2

Under the Rug
3

Apply!

Every single use of the word *love* in 1 John is agape! Do you understand the significance of this? John says that we are known by our *love*. He says that those who *love* the Lord are His children. This is the kind of *love* that is only able to be done by the Spirit. It surprises others. It is obvious because it is so opposite of what we, as men and women in the flesh, would do. Look at all of these other passages that are proclaiming the same kind of *love*...not brotherly, kindhearted *love*, but God-given and power-provided agape *love*.

Matthew 5:43-44 _____

_____

Matthew 22:37 _____

_____

John 3:16 _____

_____

2 Corinthians 5:14-15* _____

_____

Ephesians 5:1-4* _____

_____

As we wrap up looking at God's *agape love*, we could use John 3:16 as the greatest example of *agape love*. God loved us unconditionally, knowing what we **needed**; a payment for sin. He loved us while we were yet sinners. He gave us what we **needed** most.

APPLY!

Have you seen the acronym "WWJD"? It represents the saying, "What would Jesus do?" and can be found on bumper stickers and bracelets. You may have known about the saying, but did you know that it was coined and popularized by a 1897 classic written by Charles Monroe Sheldon? The novel, "In His Steps" is well worth reading. Check your library or online bookstores to get a copy and read this bestselling book.

Disciples are required to leave old dependencies, loyalties, and paradigms.
Money, power, and pleasure all take on very different meanings.
The first disciples left their nets. Where would the income come from now?
They left their boats. What would keep them from sinking now?
They left their father. Who would love and instruct them now?
Disciples know the answer to all three questions is "Jesus."
~ Trent Griffith ~

A . C . T . S .   P R A Y E R   T I M E

"And walk in love, as Christ loved us and gave himself up for us,
a fragrant offering and sacrifice to God."
~ Ephesians 5:2 ESV ~

A - *Adoration*_____

C - *Confession*_____

T - *Thanksgiving*_____

S - *Supplication*_____

D A Y   F O U R

ON MY KNEES:

Shhh, quiet your heart before the Lord in prayer before continuing your study of the word *love*.

Pray. "How AWESOME, Lord, to know that You can do ALL things, and that NO purpose of Yours can be thwarted. This is such a word from You through Your Word. Praise You, Lord! For no man, whether strong or weak, wealthy or poor, wise or foolish can thwart Your purposes!" (Job 42:2)

Write. Write 1 John 4:20-21 to finish up your copy of 1 John , Chapter 4.

Read. Open your Bible to 1 John 4 and read all 21 verses.

Apply!

INVESTIGATIVE STUDY
UNDER THE RUG
CROSS REFERENCES - "LOVE"

Agape love is a charge to act with our will and mind, versus how we feel in our hearts. So when someone irritates us or hurts us, we are still commanded to *love* them. How much easier this command should be when it involves the Lord, for He is perfect. He *loves* us regardless of our performance. Today, we will look at additional *love* cross references.

What were the important words that Deuteronomy 6:5-7 directed Israel to teach the children?

_____

Read 1 Thessalonians 4:9-10. The first instance of *love* in this passage is *phileo*, but the second is *agape*. What is said in verse 10? _____

Read and summarize what you learn about *love* in Luke 11:42. _____

_____

Read and summarize what you learn about *love* in John 13:34-35. _____

_____

Read and summarize what you learn about *love* in John 15:10. _____
_____

      Love is so important that God gave us His definition using an entire chapter of 1 Corinthians. He wants us to clearly understand the attributes of **agape love**. If we are going to show others Jesus' *love*, we need to know how *love* responds and reaches out. This chapter reveals how to *love*.

      Do the activities below. (If you are using the King James Version, look for the word **charity**)

☐   Read 1 Corinthians 13.

☐   Circle or put a heart around the word *love (charity)* using a red colored pencil.

☐   Underline the all the things that *love (charity)* does.

      Ok, so now, *love* the Lord your God with all your heart, soul and will. And, *love* others the same way. Child of God, there is no way to accomplish this standard of *love* without the Spirit of God. May the Lord teach us how to *love* as He does. Go before Him in prayer.

A.C.T.S. PRAYER TIME

"But as it is written: 'Eye has not seen, nor ear heard, nor have entered into the heart of man the things which God has prepared for those who love Him.'"
~ 1 Corinthians 2:9 NKJV ~

A - *Adoration* _____

C - *Confession* _____

T - *Thanksgiving* _____

S - *Supplication* _____

D A Y   F I V E

ON MY KNEES:

What is on your agenda for the day, this season…your life? As you sit down for your time with the Lord today be sure to run things by Him before you begin our summary of 1 John 4.

Pray. "Lord, You know all things. You know all the details of my life and how I am juggling them. Help me to discern between the things that I hold onto and those that need to be let go so that my priorities are right, and so that they match up with the things You have for me. I do not want to live by my agenda – I want Yours! I want to be able to dwell in Your presence and love as You do. In Your loving name, I pray, amen.

Write. Take a few minutes to review Chapter 4. Are there any references to God? Mark them with the appropriate symbols.

Read. Pull up your boot straps and read through the entire book of 1 John before moving to your "Day 10 Diagram".

INVESTIGATIVE STUDY

Aerial View
book
1

Streetview
2

Under the Rug
3

Apply!

INVESTIGATIVE STUDY
1-2-3 SUMMARIZE: CHAPTER 4

You have completed the study of another chapter of 1 John. Once again, we will summarize the main theme, Greek words and attributes that the Lord has taught us by completing a Day 10 Diagram. Before you being to work through Chapter 4, briefly look at your first three Diagrams.

☐ To begin, look at the top of the Day 10 Diagram. Fill in the chapter number. Look at Week 1, Day 5 for the original title you created for 1 John 4. Review what you wrote and refine your title with the new insights that you have learned over the last 10 days.

☐ Next, which verse from the chapter do you think was the "key verse?"

☐ On the right of the page, transfer the Greek word *agape* and its definition on the first two lines. Then, place the other three Greek words for love and their definitions on the next three lines.

☐ On the bottom of the Diagram page, transfer the most important things that you learned about God through marking the references about Him on your "Write!" pages.

We learned in 1 John 4 that God is love. As we abide in Christ, His love grows strong in and through us just like this mighty 1 Corinthians 13 tree. Our young sister in Christ is studying that chapter of the Bible as she rests in the refreshing shelter of God's *agape love*. Write the six qualities that love IS, found in 1 Corinthians 13, on the ripe fruit in the branches of the tree. Write the nine qualities that 1 Corinthians says love IS NOT beside the rotten, fallen apples scattered on the ground.

Those bad apples more aptly characterize the "Darkness" of the world- add that label on the storm clouds hovering over the horizon.   In Chapter 4 of his letter, what four descriptions did John give for those who don't belong to God? Write them on the lines below the dark clouds. (Hint: Verses 1, 3 and 20)

The darkness can't diminish the beauty and strength of God's incredible love, however. Along the sturdy trunk and branches of the tree, trace the outline of the cross, because the cross of Christ is God's greatest demonstration of His sacrificial love.   In the heart on the trunk, "carve" John's message in 1 John 4:10 about Who loved whom first. How wonderful that we also can rest in God's eternal love, day by day, and then share His kind of love with all those around us!

A . C . T . S .   P R A Y E R   T I M E

"I will bless the LORD who has counseled me; indeed, my mind instructs me in the night. I have set the LORD continually before me; because He is at my right hand, I will not be shaken. Therefore my heart is glad and my glory rejoices; my flesh also will dwell securely."
~ Psalm 16:7-9 NASB ~

A - *Adoration*_____

C - *Confession*_____

T - *Thanksgiving*_____

S - *Supplication*_____

"Disciples follow Jesus together. Look around. If you are not surrounded by other disciples, YOU ARE PROBABLY NOT A DISCIPLE. Who are your closest friends? Are they following Jesus? If not, you need some new friends. A disciple seeks out and listens to others who have walked with Jesus longer than he or she has. Disciples pursue relationships with others to teach them the disciplines of following Jesus in practical ways. Disciples mentor and encourage one another in Bible study, prayer, marriage counseling, family counseling, money and time management."
~ Trent Griffith ~

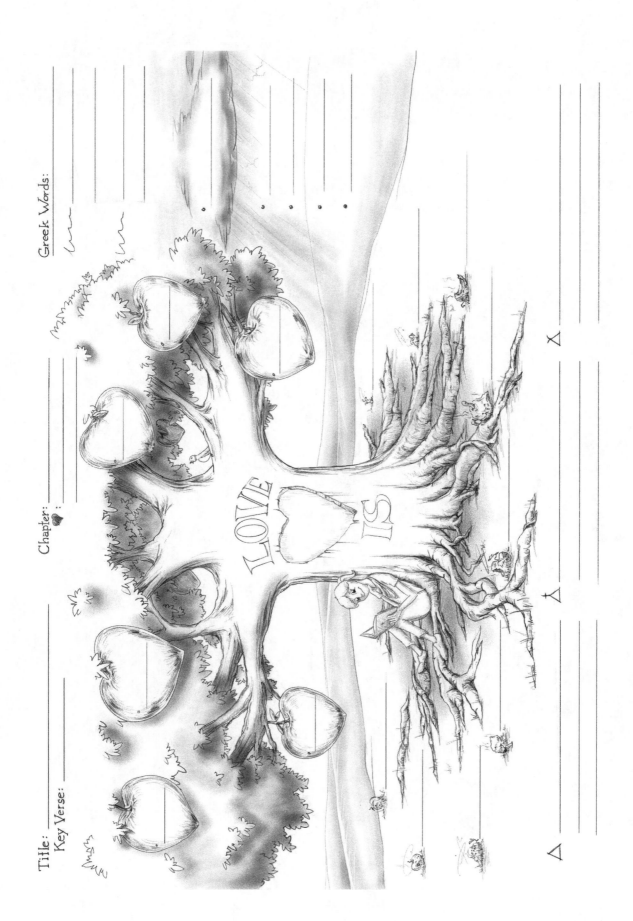

Title:

Key Verse:

Chapter: :

Greek Words:

249

Martin Luther: Table Talk

Who sits at your dinner table? Through the years, Reformer Martin Luther and his wife Katharina hosted many students, famous reformers, and others at their home in Germany. The conversations often became so spirited that many of the guests took notes. Some of these conversations were later compiled in Table Talk, *still one of Luther's most popular books.*

This week and next, our Shelby Kennedy Foundation representatives Anne (13) and Grace (9) visit the Luther home to ask the special questions inquiring Sword Study minds want to know.

Anne: Dr. Luther, of course I know who you are, but could you give our Sword Study students some insight into how God uses you?

Luther: Most gladly, my child. First of all, I identify myself as a teacher of truth. In the same way that I host great thinkers at my table, our world plays host to any number of lies. I see it as my calling to combat those lies as I stand for the truths of God's Word.

Grace: But why would people lie, Dr. Luther? I don't understand.

Luther: Ahh, of course you would not comprehend this, dear one. Why do people lie? Because of the curse of sin and death that hangs over this world. Because the evil one comes to steal, kill and destroy. And because men love to believe they are right at the expense of anything or anyone else.

Anne: But isn't it important to get along with others, Dr. Luther? I hear you started some pretty big arguments in your day.

Luther: Someone else asked me about that, so I'll give you the answer he received: "Peace if possible. Truth at all costs." In other words, I find it more important to speak the truth than to agree with others—who may or may not have a strong commitment to the truths of God's Word.

Grace: How did you start exploring the truth, sir?

Luther: I believe I was born to explore the truth—in Eiseben, Germany on November 10, 1843. My father sent me to Latin school and then to the University of Ehrfurst to study law.

Anne: Latin school? What's that?

Luther: Simply a school for younger pupils, my dear. This one taught the Ten Commandments, the Lord's Prayer, basic Latin grammar and the parts of the Bible used in church services at that time.

Grace: I study Latin, too, but not quite that much.

Luther: Another time, perhaps we should have a conversation in Latin. In any case, God used this early schooling to prepare me for His purposes.

Anne: You studied law. Did you become a lawyer?

Luther: As I said, God prepared me for His purposes. One evening, on my way back to school from my parents' home, a thunderstorm trapped me and a bolt of lightning struck the ground nearby. I fell to my knees, crying out, "Help me, St. Anne! I will become a monk!"

Grace: Were you scared of the storm, Dr. Luther?

Luther: Not nearly as scared of the storm as of our God. I had already been seeking Him and questioning His desires for my life. The storm and the lightning moved me toward a decision. I gave away everything I owned and entered a monastery—a place where I could live with others devoted to religious life.

Anne: And were you? Devoted to religious life, I mean?

Luther: Yes, I was. And that was part of the problem.

Grace: But how could that be a problem? Weren't you doing what God wanted you to do?

Luther: I thought I was. I was doing everything I could to try to please God: fasting, praying, and even going without good food or warm blankets. But as I spent more time studying the Scriptures, I realized my ideas of being godly looked different than God's true desires. I read, "The righteous shall live by faith" (Romans 1:17) and wondered how I could ever be righteous. But all the while, God was drawing me to Himself.

Anne: So did you move out of the monastery?

Luther: Not quite yet. My superior ordered me to become a student, so I studied and then taught theology at the University of Wittenberg. In the process, God showed me the only way to achieve righteousness was through His gift of faith. At long last, I knew I was born again. I wanted to share my learning with my others. I wanted them to know the truth!

Grace: And that kind of teaching got you in trouble, didn't it?

Luther: Yes, it did. But again—I prefer to stand for the truth. I became so passionate about the importance of faith alone as a means of grace, so burdened about the need for the common man to read the Scriptures, and so angry with the corrupt practices of the Church that on October 31, 1517, I nailed 95 Theses (statements of truth) to the door of the church at Wittenberg. Some call this the beginning of the Protestant Reformation.

Anne: Wow. When you stand for the truth, you really stand for the truth, don't you, Dr. Luther? I guess it's time to close our interview for now. But we'll be back again next week with some more fascinating Table Talk.

D A Y   O N E

ON MY KNEES:

You are rounding the corner and heading for home as we begin this week and the final chapter of 1 John. You have been a diligent student of the Word. As the eyes of the Lord move to and fro looking for those who seek after Him, may He continue to witness your faithful heart! Once again, begin on your knees.

Pray. "God, You are the God who sees all things. El Roi, as the Jewish people proclaim. Look into my heart and convict me of the areas that I need refined. Speak to me through the words of 1 John 5. If there is anything that I am holding onto that is not of You, remove it. I want Your thoughts to override mine. Bless me today. Amen."

Write. Begin your new chapter by writing 1 John 5:1-2 on the new chapter page of your "My Copy of 1 John" pages.

Read. As we start the last chapter of 1 John, take the extra time today to read all five chapters together in one sitting.

INVESTIGATIVE STUDY

Aerial View **1**

Streetview **2**

Under the Rug **3**

Apply!

INVESTIGATIVE STUDY
STREETVIEW: CHAPTER 5

Place your interviewer hat back on and work through the "Who, What, Why, Where, When, Which and How" questions of 1 John 5.

Who?

Who is born of God? (verse 1): _____

Who loves the child of God? (verse 1): _____

Who overcomes the world? (verse 4): _____

Who overcomes the world? (verse 5): _____

Who came by water and blood? (verse 6): _____

Who bears witness/testimony? (verses 7-8): _____

Who has the witness/testimony in him? (verse 10): _____

Who gives eternal life? (verse11): _____

What?

What is the love of God? (verse 3): _____

What has overcome the world? (verse 4): _____

What three are in agreement concerning Jesus? (verse 8): _____

What is sin? (verse 17): _____

Why?

Why does the Spirit bear witness? (verse 7): _____

Why was 1 John written? (verse 13): _____

Where?

Where is eternal life? (verse 11): _____

Where does the world lie? (verse 19): _____

When?

When we love God and do His commandments, what can we know? (verse 2): _____
_____

When does God hear our prayers? (verse 14): _____
_____

Which?

Which witness/testimony is greater? (verse 9): _____

Which person has the witness/testimony in him? (verse 10): _____

How?

How do we know that we love the children of God? (verse 2): _____
_____

How is victory over the world accomplished? (verse 4): _____

How can we know that God will hear us? (verse 14): _____

How should we handle idols? (verse 21): _____

APPLY!

What is an idol?

An idol is anything that we place before God, anything that creeps up the importance scale and surpasses our focus on God. In Leviticus, God states over and over and over, "Love the Lord, your God, with all your heart, and mind, and soul." We see the words, "You shall have NO other gods before Me" as well.

Is there anything that you find yourself spending more time, money or effort towards than your relationship with Christ or eternal things? Where are your thoughts? What do they focus on most? If something popped into your mind at this last question, try taking it away from yourself this week. The stronger your thought of "WHOA! I can't stop or miss _____," the sooner you should turn it off, walk away and fast from it!
　　　　(fill in the blank)

Use your prayer time today to honestly evaluate if there is anything you are placing ahead of God, or that is taking away from your relationship with God. If you can't think of a thing, ask Him to put a spotlight on anything that you aren't seeing.

A.C.T.S. PRAYER TIME

"O praise the Lord, all ye nations: praise him, all ye people. For his merciful kindness is great toward us: and the truth of the Lord endureth for ever. Praise ye the Lord."
~ Psalm 117:1-2 KJV ~

A - Adoration_____

C - Confession_____

T - Thanksgiving_____

S - Supplication_____

D A Y   T W O

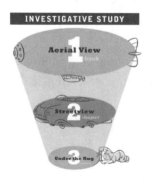

Apply!

INVESTIGATIVE STUDY
STREETVIEW: CHAPTER 5

John proclaims, "The Holy Spirit is a witness," "The Father, the Word and the Holy Spirit are witnesses," "All three are witnessing," and, "Even more, the spirit, water and blood witness and agree"…. "Everyone agrees!"

"Wait!….What does everyone agree about, John?!?"

Ordinarily, when we want to prove a case or win a debate, we state our position and then proceed with our documentation and/or witnesses to prove our case. John changes the order of the normal case presentation. First, he presents his witness list, and then in verse 11, he reveals his case statement (record or testimony).

Today we are going to focus on six verses of 1 John 5 to uncover the greatest truth of all…the record of God giving us eternal life through His son, Jesus. In 1 John 5:6-11, the Greek words **martureo** and **marturia** (Strong's Number 3140 and 3141) represent a verb, meaning "witness," and a noun, meaning " a witness." They are translated as different words depending on your Bible translation. The words are witness, record, testify and testimony.

First, look at passages on the next two pages. Chose the translation that you use and mark all of the words you find for "witness," both verbs and nouns.

Next (on the same page), underline the record, in verse 11, that John wanted everyone to know.

John's emphasis on witnesses surrounding his declaration of eternal life through Jesus is important to His readers, and to us today. Our flesh demands proof and the Word of God proclaims, I AM. Search the Scriptures for the following passages and note what additional information you learn about witnesses from them.

Deuteronomy 19:15: _____

Matthew 18:15-20:

a. _____

b. _____

John 5:31-37: _____

John 8:13-18: _____

John 15:26-27: _____

Turn to the Lord in prayer. Focus your prayer time around the Good News, backed by the only vital Witnesses, of eternal life as it is the ultimate fellowship with Jesus, the Father and fellow believers!

A.C.T.S. PRAYER TIME

"For great is the Lord, and greatly to be praised; He is to be feared above all gods. For all the gods of the peoples are worthless idols, but the Lord made the heavens."
~ Psalm 96:4-5 ESV ~

A - Adoration_____

C - Confession_____

T - Thanksgiving_____

S - Supplication_____

[6]This is he that came by water and blood, even Jesus Christ; not by water only, but by water and blood. And it is the Spirit that beareth witness, because the Spirit is truth. [7]For there are three that bear record in heaven, the Father, the Word, and the Holy Ghost: and these three are one. [8]And there are three that bear witness in earth, the spirit, and the water, and the blood: and these three agree in one. [9]If we receive the witness of men, the witness of God is greater: for this is the witness of God which he hath testified of his Son. [10]He that believeth on the Son of God hath the witness in himself: he that believeth not God hath made him a liar; because he believeth not the record that God gave of his Son. [11]And this is the record, that God hath given to us eternal life, and this life is in his Son.

~ 1 John 5:6-11 KJV ~

[6]This is He who came by water and blood—Jesus Christ; not only by water, but by water and blood. And it is the Spirit who bears witness, because the Spirit is truth. [7]For there are three that bear witness in heaven: the Father, the Word, and the Holy Spirit; and these three are one. [8]And there are three that bear witness on earth: the Spirit, the water, and the blood; and these three agree as one. [9]If we receive the witness of men, the witness of God is greater; for this is the witness of God which He has testified of His Son. [10]He who believes in the Son of God has the witness in himself; he who does not believe God has made Him a liar, because he has not believed the testimony that God has given of His Son. [11]And this is the testimony: that God has given us eternal life, and this life is in His Son.

~ 1 John 5:6-11 NKJV ~

[6]This is the One who came by water and blood, Jesus Christ; not with the water only, but with the water and with the blood. It is the Spirit who testifies, because the Spirit is the truth. [7]For there are three that testify: [8]the Spirit and the water and the blood; and the three are in agreement. [9]If we receive the testimony of men, the testimony of God is greater; for the testimony of God is this, that He has testified concerning His Son. [10]The one who believes in the Son of God has the testimony in himself; the one who does not believe God has made Him a liar, because he has not believed in the testimony that God has given concerning His Son. [11]And the testimony is this, that God has given us eternal life, and this life is in His Son.

~ 1 John 5:6-11 NASB ~

[6]This is he who came by water and blood—Jesus Christ; not by the water only but by the water and the blood. And the Spirit is the one who testifies, because the Spirit is the truth. [7]For there are three that testify: [8]the Spirit and the water and the blood; and these three agree. [9]If we receive the testimony of men, the testimony of God is greater, for this is the testimony of God that he has borne concerning his Son. [10]Whoever believes in the Son of God has the testimony in himself. Whoever does not believe God has made him a liar, because he has not believed in the testimony that God has borne concerning his Son. [11]And this is the testimony, that God gave us eternal life, and this life is in his Son.

~ 1 John 5:6-11 ESV ~

DAY THREE

ON MY KNEES:

Are storms rumbling in your area? Not the earthly, weather type, but the storms and trials of life that the Lord puts in our paths to train and disciple us in His ways and to show others His glory. If you are in a quiet, still place in your life, maybe there are fellow believers that are battling the raging waves. Go before the Lord in praise. Yes, praise that He is an intimate God who desires us to draw near to Him even through the use of trials. He is not the "far away spirit" the Gnostic philosopher would proclaim He is, but the caring Father that He proclaims Himself to be in the pages of His Word.

Pray. "Lord, I am struggling today. Sometimes - often, lately - it is hard to understand and see the big picture of all that is happening in and around me. Help me to trust Your Word and Your character. You promise that You will never leave me. You promise that You are working to perfect me to be more like Jesus. As you refine the rough corners of my flesh, give me the strength to walk in such a way that others see Your glory proclaimed. Shine through my circumstances today and refresh me in 1 John's words. Amen."

Write. 1 John 5: 6-8 is your next set of verses. Write them on the lines of your pages. Consider using a blue pen or colored pencil for the word "water."

Read. Once again, please read Chapter 5 of 1 John.

Apply!

INVESTIGATIVE STUDY
STREETVIEW: CHAPTER 5

Yesterday, as we investigated the witnesses of Jesus, the first two were "water and blood." Initially, they are mentioned in verse 6 and then repeated again in verse 7 and 8. We are going to zoom in on these two for the next couple of days. We will begin with the water.

The water stands for baptism. Jesus was baptized. He calls us to be baptized.

Baptism

In order to understand baptism, we will look to the Scriptures for the basic definition through example. The main "baptizer" before Jesus' arrival was John the Baptist as he was called in Luke 7:33. He should not be confused with our author of 1 John because they are not the same person. Baptism stemmed from the Levitical washings, which were purification from sin and accomplished by the sinner. The early washings under the law did not include repentance of sin, but the water did symbolize the washing away of sin. A New Testament summary of a baptism can be found in Mark 1:1-8. Read the passage and then answer the detailed questions below.

What was the message before the baptism in verse 4?_____

Who was baptizing in verse 5? _____

Also according to verse 5, where was he baptizing those who confessed their sins? _____
_____

According to verse 8, with what did John baptize the people? _____
_____

Turn to the passages and note the details of baptism. Who was baptized, how were they baptized and when they were baptized?

Matthew 3:4-6

Who? _____
How? _____
When? _____

Matthew 28:19:

Who? _____
How? _____
When? _____

Acts 2:38-41

Who? _____
How? _____
When? _____

Acts 8:12-13

Who? _____
How? _____
When? _____

Acts 8:1, 14, 36-38

Who? _____

How? _____

When? _____

Acts 9:17-18

Who? _____

How? _____

When? _____

Baptism symbolizes the cleansing of our heart from sin, as well as death to our past as a new creature in Christ. As public declaration of our relationship with God through our belief in Jesus Christ, baptism declares our walk in the light with the Light. We are victors over sin with the help of the Holy Spirit. We are active in fellowship with God and have power over the bondage of sin's slavery.

APPLY!

Have you been baptized?

Baptism's main purpose is to show one's agreement to join in fellowship with Christ, His death to self and sin, and resurrection to eternal fellowship with the Father.

Recalling your baptism can be a great way to refresh your excitement in the Lord. Take a few minutes to write your story below.

_____

_____

_____

_____

_____

_____

A.C.T.S. PRAYER TIME

"For ye are all the children of God by faith in Christ Jesus. For as many of you as have been baptized into Christ have put on Christ."
~ Galatians 3:26-27 KJV ~

A - Adoration_____

C - Confession_____

T - Thanksgiving_____

S - Supplication_____

DIGGING DEEPER

Investigate the roots of baptism in Leviticus 14. Note the similarities and differences in the space below.

_____

_____

_____

_____

_____

DAY FOUR

ON MY KNEES:

Did you realize that the sun came up today? Depending on where you are and what the weather was like today, you may not have visibly seen it, but it came up, didn't it? Hosea 6 says just as sure as the dawn comes, so is the faithfulness of our God. Never, not once has the sun stayed in for a break. Never has it decided the day looks like too much. Never has it wearied of the same old routine. Go to your ever-faithful God. He is waiting for you as surely as the sun rose this morning.

Pray. "Indeed, Lord, You are faithful. You are faithful when I am not. I find so much comfort in knowing Your character and that it never changes. As people, we are so unpredictable and undependable. I am so thankful that I can depend on You, and in turn, have Your strength to walk through my days. I can face all circumstances and people in the way that You desire. I have Your Spirit within me. Help me not to quench Your work in my life today. Speak to me through Your words in 1 John 5."

Write. Write 1 John 5:9-10.

Read. Once again, read 1 John 5.

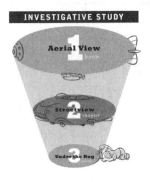

Apply!

INVESTIGATIVE STUDY
STREETVIEW: CHAPTER 5

Now that you focused on the "water witness" of Jesus yesterday, let's zoom in on the blood. First though, we need to make the connection between the two. Looking at the baptism of Jesus will make that connection.

Jesus' Baptism

While we could choose any of the Gospels' record of this event, it seems appropriate to hear our author's version. Turn to the account of Jesus' baptism in John 1:26-34. Summarize the events as you did the other examples of baptism.

Who? _____

How? _____

When? _____

Are there any differences between our baptism and Jesus' baptism? What does Jesus say in Mark 10:38-39? _____

Ah, here is where the water and the blood unite. Do you know the "cup" that Jesus spoke of? Confirm your thoughts by turning to Mark 14:35-36 and note what the cup was here: _____
_____

Using a dictionary, write the definition of propitiation on the lines: _____
_____

Jesus' blood was our propitiation.

Summarize what you learn in the following passages regarding the blood of Christ.

Romans 3:25 _____

1 Corinthians 10:15-17 _____

Hebrews 2:17 _____

Hebrews 9:13-15 _____

1 Peter 1:18-20 _____

1 John 4:10 _____

A.C.T.S. PRAYER TIME

*"Therefore everyone who confesses Me before men, I will also
confess him before My Father who is in heaven."*
~ Matthew 10:32 NASB ~

A - *Adoration* _____

C - *Confession* _____

T - *Thanksgiving* _____

S - *Supplication* _____

DAY FIVE

ON MY KNEES:

Ta Da! You have finished to another week of Bible study. Isn't studying His Word so different from studying or reading the knowledge of man? As you read a book or study a textbook, you must constantly be evaluating its content for truth through the lenses of God's Word. Whereas, when you study "the Truth", you can freely soak in each word. Let's begin in prayer.

Pray. "Truth. You are truth. You speak truth. I am sanctified by Your truth. Lord, I want to be able to discern truth in my life. Fix Your words upon my mind so that when I come across darkness in the books I read, the things I see or the activities I witness, I will know when to flee. I want to walk in the light. Show me more of Your ways. In Jesus' name, I pray. Amen."

Write. Open, or let your Bible voluntarily open to 1 John. Turn to Chapter 5 and write verses 11 through 13.

Read. Stand up. Walk to a nearby bright spot. Read 1 John 5 aloud.

INVESTIGATIVE STUDY
STREETVIEW: CHAPTER 5

INVESTIGATIVE STUDY

Aerial View

Streetview

Under the Rug

Apply!

We have found a repetitive accusation throughout John's letter. Have you ever heard it said that a person has used up their checkbook of trust by their deceitfulness? When a person's actions do not match with their words, there is a problem. They are lying. They are liars. John highlights several examples within this small book.

Look up each of the 1 John examples and circle the word "lie" or "liars" in black. If you see the word "truth," circle it in yellow. Note something you learn about lying or liars on the lines after each verse.

1 John 1:6 _____

1 John 1:8 _____

1 John 1:10 _____

1 John 2:4 _____

1 John 2:22 _____

1 John 2:27 _____

1 John 4:20 _____

1 John 5:10 _____

There are numerous descriptions and details surrounding liars within Scripture. We have given you a few here to deepen your understanding of how the Word of God views the liar, or one who is untruthful. Find the passage and note what you hear concerning the liar, lies, and deceit, and their rival: truth.

Psalm 15:1-5 _____

Psalm 62:4 _____

Psalm 101:7 _____

Psalm 119:160* _____

Proverbs 14:5 _____

Proverbs 19:22 _____

Habakkuk 2:18 ("falsehood" in NASB) _____

John 8:31-32* _____

John 8:43-45 _____

A.C.T.S. PRAYER TIME

A - Adoration_____

C - Confession_____

T - Thanksgiving_____

S - Supplication_____

Martin Luther: Table Talk (continued)

A continuation of last week's interview of Dr. Martin Luther with Shelby Kennedy Foundation representatives, Anne and Grace.

Anne: Here we are again, dining with Dr. Luther and getting his insights on some of the theological issues of his day.

Luther: You young ladies are always welcome to share our table—and join our Table Talk.

Grace: The last time we spoke with you, Dr. Luther, you mentioned "corrupt practices of the Church" as something you spoke out against. What did you mean?

Luther: I feared the Church had grown far too interested in building her reputation—and her bank account—and not interested enough in building God's reputation or adding souls to His kingdom account.

Anne: What could a Church do that would be so wrong?

Luther: Plenty. The leaders of the Church were selling what they called "indulgences." They said these slips of paper would free a soul from a place they called purgatory, an imaginary place between life and death. A person would have to buy many of these expensive indulgences in order to buy anyone's way into heaven.

Grace: Now, that's just weird.

Luther: Exactly. And not only that, it was wrong, too. Scripture clearly states that salvation comes by faith alone. So my 95 Theses argued against the use of the indulgences and other evils.

Anne: And the Church wasn't happy with those arguments, correct?

Luther: "Not happy" understates the truth. Because of the invention of the printing press, copies my 95 Theses traveled throughout Germany within two weeks and throughout Europe within a month.

Grace: So I'm guessing the Church was even more unhappy then?

Luther: Yes, indeed. Liars want nothing to do with the truth. In October, 1518, they asked me to recant—to deny what I had stated in the 95 Theses. I refused to do it unless Scripture proved me wrong.

Anne: And of course, it did not.

Luther: Of course. Later that year, I made it known to the people that the Bible did not give the pope (head of the Church) the exclusive right to interpret Scripture. People could read the Bible for themselves.

Grace: Ooh, I bet that made the pope angry.

Luther: Oh, yes. In 1520, he sent a letter that threatened to excommunicate me, or throw me out of the Church. I burned it.

Anne: Wow, you have no problem standing for the truth, do you?

Luther: None whatsoever. And the pope stood his ground, too. Not long after that, the church excommunicated me. They also banned my writings through a statement called the Edict of Worms. They said no one should read them because I was a heretic, or enemy of the faith.

Grace: Did that stop people from reading your work, Dr. Luther?

Luther: It had the opposite effect. In fact, now I had the freedom—and the platform, or ready audience—waiting to hear what I had to say.

Grace: And what did you have to say, Dr. Luther?

Luther: I'm honored you would ask. First, I had something important to do. I translated the New Testament into German so ordinary people could have the opportunity to read God's Word.

Anne: You mean they couldn't do that before?

Luther: Oh, no. My New Testament was published in 1522. Before that, the Scriptures were all in Latin, and only priests could read them. In this way, the Church kept a tight control on her people, because few knew what the Bible really said. I wanted them to be able to explore God's Word for themselves.

Grace: That sounds like a great idea to me.

Luther: Thank you. I had some more great ideas, too. I wrote hymns for the church like "A Mighty Fortress Is Our God" that explored the great truths of the faith. I started my own church, the first in what became the Lutheran denomination. In 1525, I married my dear Katharina von Bora, a former nun. Together we committed to live a life of obedience to God's Word. And in 1532, the Old Testament—which I had also translated into German, the language of the people—was published.

Anne: So it sounds like you keep busy with ministry and with your marriage.

BOOK OF 1 JOHN

Luther: Very much so. Katharina and I had six children together, three boys and three girls. I continue to teach in the university setting and through my home, where we have boarded and mentored more than a thousand students through the years. Some of my assistants—Philip Melanchthon, for example—have gone on to be important theologians in their own right.

Grace: So if you were going to sum up your life for us, how would you do it, sir?

Luther: I would have to say two things: "Here I stand" (my statement at the Diet of Worms, when I refused to recant the 95 Theses) and "Peace if possible. Truth at all costs." You cannot have real faith without truth. And I am grateful to the God who showed me the way out of darkness and into truth and light.

Anne: Grace and I are grateful for all you have done to bring truth to the world, Dr. Luther. Thank you for sharing your Table Talk with us.

D A Y   O N E

ON MY KNEES:

Are there little voices around you? Has the Lord blessed you with younger siblings or children in your home? What a blessing it is to witness the energy and excitement children bring to our lives. When something harms or threatens to harm a young friend of ours, oh, how quickly we can become "mother-bearish." As we continue studying 1 John, we can hear John and thus, the Spirit's gentle, firm and protective tone calling us to God's ways rather than man's ways. Let's pray before we begin our study.

Pray. "Lord, I am so comforted to know that You are my mountain range, a hedge of enormous protection. I call upon You. Give ear to my voice. May my prayers be as a pleasing fragrance before You, the lifting up of my hands and heart as an offering. Keep my eyes upon You and my trust focused on You. You are my refuge and will not leave me defenseless. Use Your words today to strengthen me. (Psalm 141)

Write. Please write 1 John 5:14-15.

Read. Read or listen to 1 John 5. If you are able, record yourself reading 1 John 5. Your recording would be a great gift for a younger Sword Study student!

INVESTIGATIVE STUDY

Aerial View 1

Streetview 2

Under the Rug 3

Apply!

INVESTIGATIVE STUDY
UNDER THE RUG:
WORD STUDY - "BELIEVE"

We have arrived at the last chapter of 1 John as we descend to our UNDER THE RUG level of investigation. You may have circled a word or two that you felt would be worthwhile as a Key Word. The two words that we have chosen for Chapter 5 were chosen for their importance to John's message rather than for repetitive use. We will begin with the word *believe* and conclude our word studies of 1 John with *understanding*.

Where do you find the word *believe* in 1 John 5? Write the references after you read the passage. Do not fill in the summary yet.

Reference: _____

Summary: _____

Reference: _____

Summary: _____

Reference: _____
Summary: _____

Reference: _____
Summary: _____

Now, read through the word study of the word **believe.**

PART A: If you were to look up the word **believe** in Strong's Concordance, you would find that the Strong's numbers assigned to it in 1 John are 4100 and 4102. We will use these numbers to look up the detailed explanation of the Greek words in Part B. Below are the transliteration (the way the word is written in English), the pronunciation, and the basic definition from the Strong's lexicon (dictionary).

4100. Believe. pist□uō. *pist-yoo□-o*, from 1402; to have faith (in, upon, or with respect to, a person or thing), i.e. credit; by impl. to entrust (espec. one's spiritual well-being to Christ):-believe (-r), commit (to trust), put in trust with.

4102. Believe. pistis. *pis□-tis*, from 3982; persuasion, i.e. credence; mor. conviction (of relig. truth, or the truthfulness of God or a relig. teacher), espec. reliance upon Christ for salvation; abstr. constancy in such profession; by extension, the system of religious (Gospel) truth itself;- assurance, belief, believe, faith, fidelity.

PART B: If you look up the number in another Greek lexicon, you can discover further explanations of the meanings of believe in Greek as seen here:

4100. **Believe**, verb; to be persuaded, rely upon, to trust, have reliance, not mere credence, fully convinced, self-surrendering fellowship, fully assured and unswerving confidence in:
    i. Something
    ii. God
    iii. Messenger from God

4102. **Believe**, translated **Faith**, noun; to win over, persuade in truth, doctrine, articles of Christian faith, such as:
    i. Christian doctrine
    ii. the Gospel
    iii. All that Christianity stands for

PART C: According to Vine's dictionary, John used the verb **pisteuo** over 99 times in his gospel of John, which was significantly more than the other gospel writers. The other writers only used it 9 or 10 times each in comparison. Armed with your new knowledge of **pisteuo**, look back at the four passages that contain the word **believe**. Write a short summary of what you learn from each of them on the lines below.

Can you find another instance of **believe** in 1 John 5, but in the form of *pistis*? Write the verse below:

_____

_____

_____

Before closing your time in prayer, skim through your handwritten copy of 1 John looking for the words **believe** and *faith*. Mark each one with a special symbol of your choosing.

A.C.T.S. PRAYER TIME

"Your lovingkindness, O LORD, extends to the heavens, Your faithfulness reaches to the skies. Your righteousness is like the mountains of God; Your judgments are like a great deep. O LORD, You preserve man and beast."
~ Psalm 36:5-6 NASB ~

A - Adoration_____

C - Confession_____

T - Thanksgiving_____

S - Supplication_____

DAY TWO

ON MY KNEES:

So, are we supposed to be our "brother's keeper," or not? Cain mockingly replied to God this way when asked about Abel's whereabouts. The verses you will write today will give you discernment concerning our brothers and sisters in Christ. Go before the Father in prayer before you write the next set of verses in 1 John 5.

Pray. "Lord, sometimes the people in my life frustrate me. I need Your insight and patience. Turn the mirror to my own actions and Your example as You work with me! I need to react, respond and reach out in ways that honor You and treat Your people in a right manner. Help me learn how to do this better. Amen."

Write. Neatly write 1 John 5:16-17 on the next lines of your "Write" pages.

Read. Grab a friend and take turns reading three or four verses of 1 John 5 until you have read the whole chapter. Pray for one another, and then carry on individually with your study.

INVESTIGATIVE STUDY

Aerial View

Streetview

Under the Rug

Apply!

INVESTIGATIVE STUDY
UNDER THE RUG:
CROSS REFERENCES - "BELIEVE"

Ready? Are you learning your way around the books of the Bible through your cross reference exercises? Today, we will travel through the Scriptures seeking additional depth to our understanding of the word *believe.* We will see the call to have faith in Christ, the people who have relied upon Christ and the attributes of faith.

Note an insight from each passage regarding *faith* and/or *believing* on the lines. Let's go!

Mark 1:14-15 _____

Mark 16:16 _____

John 3:36 _____

John 7:38-39 _____

Acts 10:38-43 _____

Hebrews 11:1 _____

James 2:18-19 _____

In 1 Peter 2:6, we hear that those who **believe** in Jesus will not be confounded nor disappointed. Jesus is our hope, our way, truth and life! Go to your prayer time proclaiming the praises of Him who called you out of the darkness into His marvelous light!

A.C.T.S. PRAYER TIME

"Blessed are those whose lawless deeds have been forgiven, and whose sins have been covered.
"Blessed is the man whose sin the Lord will not take into account."
~ Romans 4:7-8 NASB ~

A - *Adoration* _____

C - *Confession* _____

T - *Thanksgiving* _____

S - *Supplication* _____

D A Y   T H R E E

ON MY KNEES:

"I passed!" "I got an A!" Doing well on a test or quiz gives us such a great feeling of success. Getting an "A" on a test doesn't come automatically. The successful student must diligently study to do well. Can you carry this logic to your studying in the Word? If we expect to do well before the Lord and others in our daily walk, we must know what the Lord desires. We know how to walk in His light by studying His Word. Let's pray before we continue on our path to success!

Pray. "How gracious and kind You are, Lord, for giving me the Handbook to success. Thank You for providing Your Word so that I do not have to guess on how to live well. Help me to take responsibility for the failures that I have and learn from them. Open my heart to what You have to teach me today."

Write. Turn to your "My Copy of 1 John" and write 1 John 5:18-19.

Read. Before you begin your Greek word study, please read Chapter 5 of 1 John.

Apply!

INVESTIGATIVE STUDY
UNDER THE RUG:
WORD STUDY - "UNDERSTANDING"

Have you ever suddenly had a light bulb of *understanding* occur, like a lightning bolt? While other times it takes great study to gain *understanding*? The Word of God says that our hearts are deceitful and that we are not to lean on our own *understanding*. Let's look at the Greek word study of *understanding* and see what we learn about the *understanding* that John spoke of in 1 John 5.

PART A: If you were to look up the word *understanding* in Strong's Concordance, you would find that the Strong's number assigned to it in 1 John 5:20 is 1271. We will use these numbers to look up the detailed explanation of the Greek words in Part B. Below are the transliteration (the way the word is written in English), the pronunciation, and the basic definition from the Strong's lexicon (dictionary).

1271. *Understanding.* dian̄ia *dee-an̄-oy-yah*, from 1223 and 3563; deep thought, prop. the faculty (mind or its disposition), by impl. its exercise: imagination, mind, understanding.

PART B: If you look up the number in another Greek lexicon, you can discover further explanations of the meaning of *understanding* in Greek as seen here:

1.   A thinking through, mature thought; activity of thinking with the heart.

PART C: The word *understanding* is only found one time in 1 John 5. Can you find it? Write the reference and passage here:

_____
_____
_____
_____

This verse is very important. Answer all of the questions on this ONE verse.

Where did the Son of God come? _____

Why did the Son of God come? _____

What did He give us?_____

What word is repeated three times? _____

Who is the Son of God? _____

Jesus coming gives us *understanding* so that we can know the truth about God, the Father. Jesus gives us understanding in our hearts that His Father is true and gives us eternal life! Tomorrow, we will look at more verses to that tell us what we can *understand* because of Jesus.

A.C.T.S. PRAYER TIME

"Trust in the Lord with all thine heart; and lean not unto thine own understanding. In all thy ways acknowledge him, and he shall direct thy paths."
~ Proverbs 3:5-6 KJV ~

A - Adoration_____

C - Confession_____

T - Thanksgiving_____

S - Supplication_____

D A Y   F O U R

ON MY KNEES:

"The LORD is my shepherd; I shall not want." From a child's perspective, this verse can cause confusion. "I don't understand, why wouldn't I 'want' the Lord as my shepherd?" We are children of the Lord. It's interesting that we don't find the "Adults of God" mentioned in the Word. Growing in maturity, yes, but completed…nope. He is our Shepherd and we shall lack nothing, but there is always more we can learn. Go to Him in humble supplication for more wisdom.

Pray. "Jesus, You are my Good Shepherd. You offer me green pastures and quiet, still waters. Restore my soul today and guide me in a path of righteousness. I want to claim Your promises of goodness and lovingkindness in my days. I want to dwell in Your presence. Show me more of Yourself today in my word study of *understanding*."

Write. Today is noteworthy! You will finish your copy of 1 John today as you write verses 20 and 21 of 1 John 5. Well done!

Read. Re-read 1 John 5.

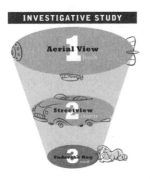

Apply!

INVESTIGATIVE STUDY
UNDER THE RUG:
CROSS REFERENCES - *"UNDERSTANDING"*

Jesus came that we might have an ***understanding*** about Him. Our ***understanding*** allows us to deeply know Him and His truth. Read the following passages that contain the word ***dianoia.*** Use the lines to note what is being ***understood***. At times translators use the words ***"mind"*** or ***"heart"*** instead of ***understanding*** for the translation of dianoia.

Matthew 22:36-40* _____

Ephesians 1:18 _____

Ephesians 4:18 _____

Colossians 1:19-22 _____

Psalm 119:125 _____
Psalm 119:169 _____

Proverbs 3:5-6 _____

Proverbs 23:23 (verses 24-25 are a bonus read!) _____

     Would you say that you have a better ***understanding*** of 1 John than you did ten weeks ago?! Oh, the blessings that the Lord gives to His diligent student! Return to your knees in prayer as you close your time in God's Word.

APPLY!

     Plan a time of fellowship around watching either the DVD of The Hiding Place or St. John in Exile with friends from church. Discuss how the main character's faith sustained them in their trials.

A.C.T.S. PRAYER TIME

"Let my cry come before You, O Lord; give me understanding according to Your word."
~ Psalm 119:169 ESV ~

A - *Adoration* _____

C - *Confession* _____

T - *Thanksgiving* _____

S - *Supplication* _____

D A Y   F I V E

ON MY KNEES:

Today, you will complete your last Day 10 Diagram. Before you begin your summary activity, go before the Lord in prayer.

Pray. "Lord, help me to slow down today. Cause me to see clearly the message of 1 John 5 as I summarize all that You have taught me. Imprint Your lessons and precepts upon my heart that I might not forget Your lessons. Help me to live them out daily. I do not want to be the person who looks in the mirror and is only temporarily affected. Change me permanently through Your power. Amen."

Write. Take a few minutes to review Chapter 5. Are there any references to God? Mark them with the appropriate symbols.

Read. Pull up your boot straps and read your entire copy of 1 John 5. Try not to get delayed by any of your own notes!

Apply!

INVESTIGATIVE STUDY
1-2-3 SUMMARIZE: CHAPTER 5

Amazing! After you complete this final Diagram, you will have a five-page, pictorial summary of the book of 1 John. Quickly, look back at the first four Diagrams to see how they lead up to this final Diagram.

☐ To begin, look at the top of the Day 10 Diagram. Fill in the chapter number. Look at Week 1, Day 5 for the original title you created for 1 John 5. Review what you wrote and refine your title with the new insights that you have learned over the last 10 days.

☐ Next, which verse from the chapter do you think was the "key verse?"

☐ On the right of the page, transfer your key Greek words from this chapter. Write the English words on the top line after the words "Greek Words." Transfer the Greek spellings and write a short definition of their meanings.

☐ On the bottom of the Diagram page, transfer the most important things that you learned about God through marking the references about Him on your "Write!" pages.

Let's join our young fellow believers as they conclude their journey through 1 John.

Since
John finishes his letter in Chapter 5 with a fervent defense of the gospel, we find them in the courtroom where the message (testimony) that God has given us eternal life in His Son, Jesus Christ, is on trial.

Right now, John is introducing the list of witnesses that testify that Jesus is the Son of God. On the chart behind John, write in each witness that he mentions in Chapter 5. The young believers know that they can rejoice in the outcome of this hearing, because they believe John's encouragement that "he who is in them is greater than he that is in the world." Write the word, "Victor" on each of their pennants, and note any three of John's descriptions of the Children of God from Chapter 5 on the blanks to the right of the believers. There are quite a few in this chapter, pick your favorites!

Though darkness glowers on the opposite side of the courtroom, the scales make it clear whose testimony holds the greater weight of truth; label each side of the scales with the two kinds of testimony that John names in verse 5:9.

In the climax of the trial, the cross of Christ gloriously prevails on the witness stand. No argument can cloud its reassuring proclamation of 1 John 5:13; in the shining starburst above the cross, write the exhortation, "Believe!" On the paper nailed to the cross, write what we can be sure of when we believe in the name of the Son of God. Conclude by filling in the final lines on the witness stand with the two words that describe Who we can know, Who we dwell in, and Who Christ is, according to verse 5:20. The case is closed, the verdict is undeniable: as believers in Jesus Christ, we can rejoice, secure in the knowledge that we will live forever with God!

A . C . T . S .   P R A Y E R   T I M E

"But as many as received Him, to them He gave the right to become
children of God, to those who believe in His name: who were born,
not of blood, nor of the will of the flesh, nor of the will of man, but of God."
~ John 1:12-13 NKJV ~

A - *Adoration*_____

C - *Confession*_____

T - *Thanksgiving*_____

S - *Supplication*_____

Title: _____

Key Verse: _____

Chapter: ___ : ___

Greek Words: _____

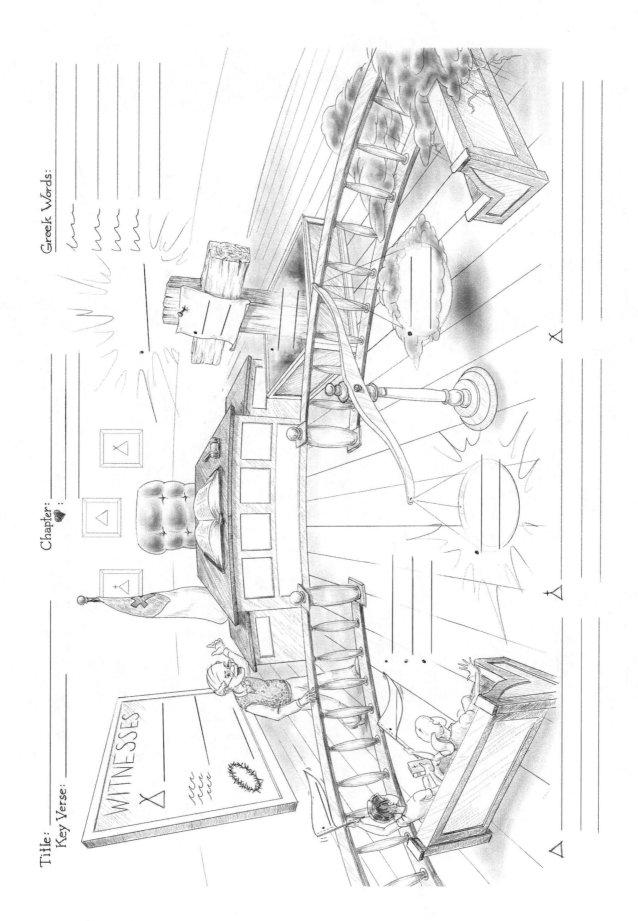

WITNESSES

287

The Return

Andrew, Karissa and Melanie walked back into the church building after telling the last of the other families good-bye. The Local Bible Bee Contest and Celebration had ended only an hour or so before.

"Can you believe how cute those little Primaries were saying their verses?" Karissa said. "I'm so glad Dad let us help with the younger children!"

"Hey, I'm still in the Primary division," Melanie protested. "And I'm not little."

"No, you're not," encouraged Andrew. "Only one more year, and you get to move up. Did you hear us cheering?"

"Oh, yes," Melanie smiled. "And Mom gave me lots of jobs, too. I liked holding Mrs. Jamieson's baby best. He's sooo cute!"

"I know!" Karissa agreed. "I loved seeing people we hadn't seen since last year's Bee. And so many new ones, too."

"And they've become our friends because of the summer Bible Bee events," Andrew added. "Without the Bee, I never would have gotten to know Nelson, Ben, and Jesse."

"You know, I think you're talking about *fellowship*," Mom added as she and Dad joined the three children. "Just like we learned about in our Sword Study."

"That's right," Andrew said, "and thanks for everything you guys did so that we could be a part of this- I know putting the Bee together was lots of work."

Dad smiled. "Yes, and we are tired. But whenever I think about all those families digging deeper into God's Word, I know it's worth it."

Just then, Mom's cell phone rang. A smile brightened her face as she saw the name that lit up her screen. "It's your grandma. I'll take the call in the sanctuary. That way, your dad and I can double-check on the cleaning," she said. "Can you find something to do?"

"Sure, Mom," Karissa answered. "No problem." Turning to her brother and sister, she suggested, "Why don't we do the same thing out here? Let's make sure it's ready for church tomorrow. We don't want them to have anything left to do."

"Sounds good," Andrew agreed. Opening a closet, he told his sisters, "Maybe I can find a—"

"Broom?" said the apostle John, stepping out of the closet and handing Andrew the needed tool.

"Wow," said Andrew and Karissa together.

"Hi!" said Melanie. "You like to show up when Mom leaves, don't you?"

"You've got me figured out," John laughed as he shook out his robe. "That closet might be fine for cleaning supplies, but it's a tight fit for me."

"We don't need encouragement this time," said Melanie. "We already did this year's Sword Study!"

"I know." John grinned. "But I want to hear what you learned."

"Did you miss the Bible Bee?" Melanie asked.

"I did," John answered. "But I'm not talking about the contest."

"What's Dad been telling us?" Andrew put in as he swept up a small dust pile. "The purpose of the Sword Study is the same as the purpose of 1 John. And that's …"

"*To know the truth!*" his sisters finished.

"That's right!" John's smile lit up the room. "Can you tell me more?"

"Fellowship," Melanie offered. "God wants us to have fellowship one with another."

"Fellowship," John mused. "Like this room? A place to eat?"

"Of course not," Melanie was grinning now. "Fellowship means partnership, true sharing. We only have real fellowship with those who know God. And we come to know God by believing in Jesus and obeying His commandments."

"You've got it!" said John.

"God also wants us to have fellowship with Him." Karissa added. "He wants us to draw near to Him through His Word. And He wants us to spend time with Him."

"You've got it, too," John affirmed.

"Excuse me, but what I've got is an idea," Andrew was sponging down the stainless steel counters. "Let's see if Dad and Mom will stop at the Shake Shoppe on the way home."

"The Shake Shoppe," John mused. "An ice cream place?"

"Yeah!" Excitement filled Melanie's voice. "My favorite!"

"But Mel," Andrew looked into his youngest sister's eyes. "This time, Dad and Mom aren't going to treat us. This time, *we'll* get them any kind of ice cream *they* want."

"Oh," Melanie gave him a big smile. "Like, 'Love one another, because love comes from God'?"

"Exactly," the others said in unison.

"I could get used to loving people that way," said Melanie. "The ice cream way!"

"Kids," Mom's voice sounded from down the hall. John vanished as suddenly as he had appeared.

The three children grinned at each other and walked over to meet their mother.

"Hey, Mom," Andrew said. "We've got an idea."

"Your dad and I have an idea, too," Mom said. "Dad thinks because you three worked so hard on your Sword Studies and helped me so much with the Local Bee, it's time for a special treat."

"A special treat?" Melanie asked. "Ice cream?"

"Something even sweeter," Mom said. "We don't know yet if any of you qualified for the National Bible Bee Competition. But no matter what, we've decided to take a trip to go to Nationals this fall. We'll make it a family vacation!"

"Yay!" "Awesome!" "I can't believe it!" the three children shouted. "When do we go?"

"It happens about mid-November," Mom said. "We'll look at the calendar. I think we can volunteer at the Bee and still take some day trips in the area. The hotel even has a water park!"

"That sounds great! And so does stopping at The Shake Shoppe on the way home," Andrew continued. "Our treat."

"Yes," Melanie added. "Because we want to have fellowship. And love one another — the ice cream way."

D A Y   O N E

ON MY KNEES:

Well done! You have been a diligent student of the Word of God! This week we are going back up to the AERIAL VIEW to review each chapter of 1 John. We will use this week to reinforce all we studied by reading our own prayers, reviewing our notes on each chapter and looking back at each chapter's "Day 10 Diagram." In addition, we will summarize all that we learn about the Lord in each chapter.

Let's begin today as we have each day, on our knees…

Pray.

Write. Write Matthew 5:14-16 on the lines below. This passage is a wonderful summary for us as children of God. If you have memorized it, write out the passage and then check it! _____

_____

_____

_____

_____

Read. Open back up to the well-worn pages of 1 John, Chapter 1 and read the chapter.

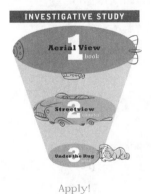

INVESTIGATIVE STUDY

Apply!

INVESTIGATIVE STUDY
AERIAL VIEW: CHAPTER 1 REVIEW

Fill in the blank Day 10 Diagram on today's last page by memory or by looking at Chapter 1 in your Bible. Afterward, look back at your Day 10 Diagram from Week 3, Day 5 for 1 John.

Look at your handwritten copy of 1 John 1. Skim through the verses looking for symbols that represent the Lord. Fill in what you learn about God under the symbols below.

God the Father

God the Son

God the Holy Spirit

_____   _____   _____

_____   _____   _____

_____   _____   _____

God the Father

God the Son

God the Holy Spirit

_____   _____   _____

_____   _____   _____

_____   _____   _____

_____   _____   _____

Keeping all that you have learned from 1 John 1 in mind, answer the questions below.

How has this chapter helped you in living your life?
_____

How has the Lord changed you because of this chapter?
_____

What attribute about God that you learned in this chapter was most reassuring to you? _____
_____

A . C . T . S .   P R A Y E R   T I M E

Review your prayers from Weeks 2 and 3. Look at all the Lord has done since you began! Close your time in prayer. Be confident that the Lord is listening to you not because you follow a pattern; He is listening to you because He loves you!

A - *Adoration* _____

C - *Confession* _____

T - *Thanksgiving* _____

S - *Supplication* _____

Greek Words:

Chapter:

Title:
Key Verse:

D A Y   T W O

ON MY KNEES:

Pray.

Write. Write Proverbs 28:13-14 in the lines below. This passage is a good cross reference to Chapter 2. If you have memorized it, write out the passage and then check it!

_____

_____

_____

_____

Read. Turn in your Bible to 1 John, Chapter 2 and read the chapter.

Apply!

INVESTIGATIVE STUDY
AERIAL VIEW: CHAPTER 2 REVIEW

Fill in the blank Day 10 Diagram on today's last page by memory or by looking at Chapter 2 in your Bible. Afterward, look back at your Day 10 Diagram from Week 5, Day 5 for 1 John.

Next, return to your handwritten copy of 1 John 2. Scan through the verses looking for symbols that represent the Lord. Note what you learned about God under the symbols below.

God the Father

God the Son

God the Holy Spirit

God the Father

God the Son

God the Holy Spirit

_____   _____   _____

_____   _____   _____

_____   _____   _____

Keeping all that you have learned from 1 John 2 in mind, answer the questions below.

How has this chapter helped you in living your life?
_____

How has the Lord changed you because of this chapter?
_____

What attribute about God that you learned in this chapter was most encouraging to you? _____
_____

A.C.T.S. PRAYER TIME

Using one of the cross references or memory verses from Weeks 4 or 5, close your time in prayer.

A - *Adoration*_____

C - *Confession*_____

T - *Thanksgiving*_____

S - *Supplication*_____

Title: _____

Key Verse: _____

Chapter: ___ : ___

Greek Words: _____

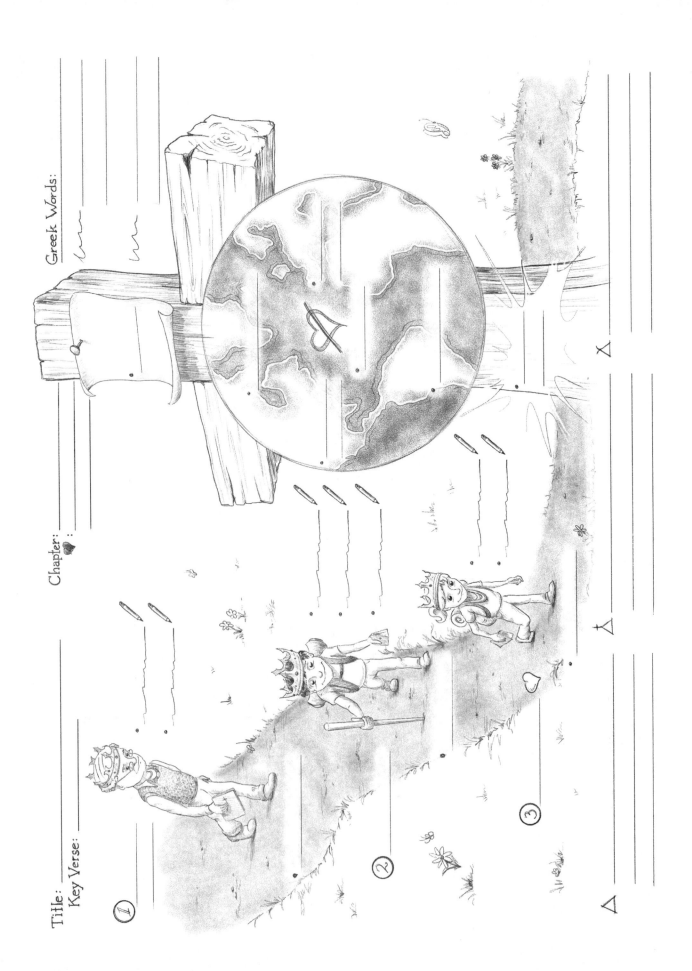

① _____

② _____

③ _____

298

D A Y T H R E E

ON MY KNEES:

Before we return to review process, go before the Lord in prayer to ask for His additional insights and memories of what we have learned from John in the third chapter of 1 John.

Pray.

Write. Write Hosea 6:3-6 on the lines below. As we draw near to the completion of our study of 1 John, this Hosea passage is such a great reminder to press on in our pursuit of knowing the Lord. We encourage you to begin considering what you will study as soon as you finish this week.

_____

_____

_____

_____

_____

Read. Read Chapter 3 of 1 John before beginning your chapter review.

INVESTIGATIVE STUDY

Apply!

INVESTIGATIVE STUDY
AERIAL VIEW: CHAPTER 3 REVIEW

Fill in the blank Day 10 Diagram on today's last page by memory or by looking at Chapter 3 in your Bible. Afterward, look back at your Day 10 Diagram from Week 7, Day 5 for 1 John.

Once again, turn to your handwritten copy of 1 John 3. Quickly go through the verses looking for symbols that represent the Lord. Fill in what you learned about God under the symbols below.

God the   Father   God the Son   God the Holy Spirit

_____   _____   _____

_____   _____   _____

_____   _____   _____

God the Father

God the Son

God the Holy Spirit

_____   _____   _____

_____   _____   _____

_____   _____   _____

_____   _____   _____

Keeping all that you have learned from 1 John 3 in mind, answer the questions below.

How has this chapter helped you in living your life?
_____

How has the Lord changed you because of this chapter?
_____

What attribute about God that you learned in this chapter was most encouraging to you? _____
_____

Over and over, we have seen the Word offer a deep relationship with God. Oh, how wonderful, how great that our holy, almighty God gives us the right to call Him Father and the privilege to call Him friend! Close in prayer.

A.C.T.S. PRAYER TIME

"And the Scripture was fulfilled which saith, Abraham believed God, and it was imputed unto him for righteousness: and he was called the Friend of God."
~ James 2:23 KJV ~

A - *Adoration* _____

C - *Confession* _____

T - *Thanksgiving* _____

S - *Supplication* _____

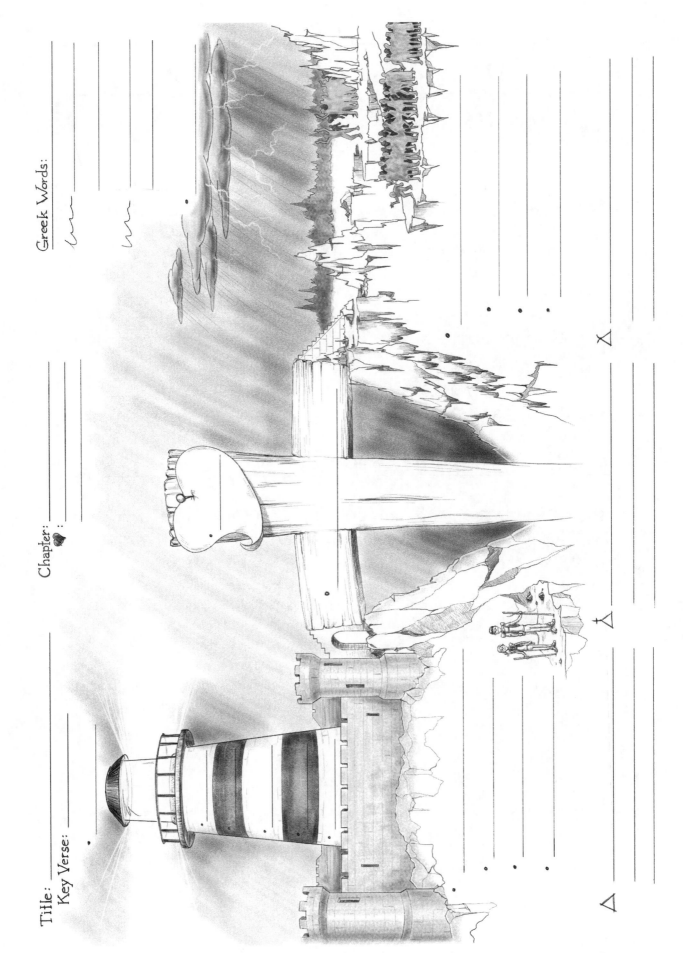

Title: _____

Key Verse: _____

Chapter: _____

Greek Words: _____

DAY FOUR

ON MY KNEES:

Pray.

Write. Write 1 John 5:13 in the lines below. Remember, child of God, you have eternal life with Jesus.   If you have memorized it, write out the passage and then check it!

_____

_____

_____

_____

Read. 1 John, Chapter 4 is your reading assignment for today.

Apply!

INVESTIGATIVE STUDY
AERIAL VIEW: CHAPTER 4 REVIEW

Fill in the blank Day 10 Diagram on today's last page by memory or by looking at Chapter 4 in your Bible. Afterward, look back at your Day 10 Diagram from Week 9, Day 5 for 1 John.

Once again, turn to your handwritten copy of 1 John 4. Quickly go through the verses looking for symbols that represent the Lord. Fill in what you learned about God under the symbols below.

God the Father　　　　　　God the Son　　　　　　God the Holy Spirit

_____　　　_____　　　_____

_____　　　_____　　　_____

God the Father

God the Son

God the Holy Spirit

_____   _____   _____

_____   _____   _____

_____   _____   _____

_____   _____   _____

_____   _____   _____

Keeping all that you have learned from 1 John 4 in mind, answer the questions below.

How has this chapter helped you in living your life?
_____

How has the Lord changed you because of this chapter?
_____

What attribute about God that you learned in this chapter was most encouraging to you? _____
_____

A . C . T . S .   P R A Y E R   T I M E

Finish your time with the Lord in prayer. Remember what you learned in Chapter 4 as you ask Jesus for strength to live for Him today and in your future.

A - *Adoration* _____

C - *Confession* _____

T - *Thanksgiving* _____

S - *Supplication* _____

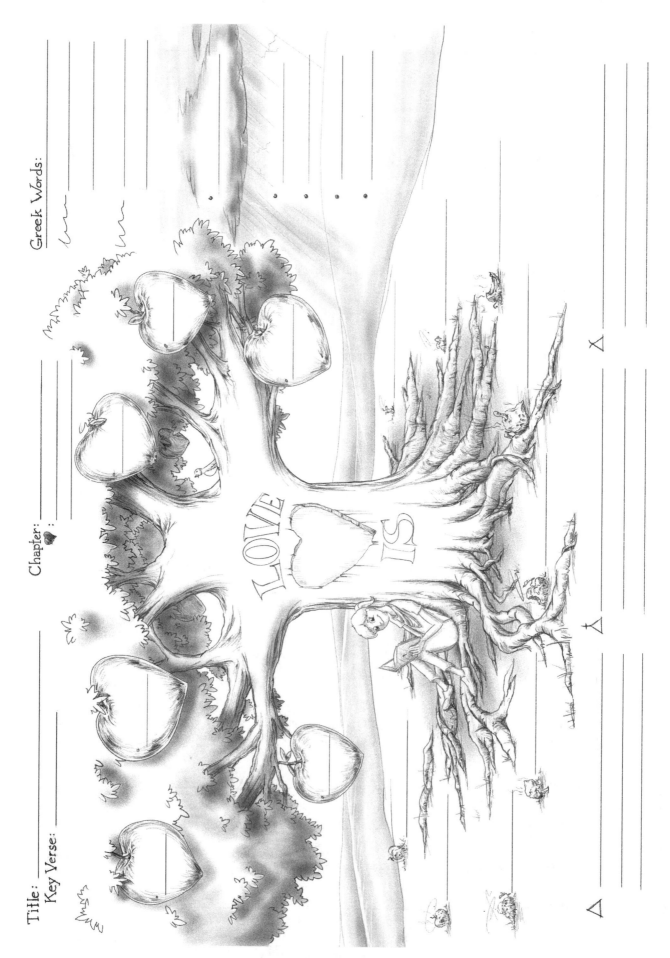

Title:

Key Verse:

Chapter: ___ : ___

Greek Words:

LOVE IS

304

DAY FIVE

ON MY KNEES:

The Lord has given you new insights. He is the Light! You have fellowshipped with Him and accomplished great things by finishing your investigative study of 1 John! Praise the Lord in prayer as you begin your final day of your Sword Study of 1 John!

Pray.

Write. Finish your Bible study as you began it 11 weeks ago by writing Jeremiah 9:23-24* on the lines below. If you have memorized it, write out the passage and then check it!

_____

_____

_____

_____

_____

_____

Read. Can you guess what we are going to ask you to do? Please read John's letter from start to finish.

INVESTIGATIVE STUDY

Apply!

INVESTIGATIVE STUDY
AERIAL VIEW: CHAPTER 5 REVIEW

Fill in the blank Day 10 Diagram on today's last page by memory or by looking at Chapter 5 in your Bible. Afterward, look back at your Day 10 Diagram from Week 11, Day 5 for 1 John.

One final time, turn to your copy of 1 John 5. Rapidly go through the verses looking for symbols that represent the Lord. Fill in what you learned about God under the symbols below.

God the Father

God the Son

God the Holy Spirit

_____   _____   _____

_____   _____   _____

_____   _____   _____

God the Father

God the Son

God the Holy Spirit

_____   _____   _____

_____   _____   _____

_____   _____   _____

_____   _____   _____

Keeping all that you have learned from 1 John 5 in mind, answer the questions below.

How has this chapter helped you in living your life?
_____

How has the Lord changed you because of this chapter?
_____

What attribute about God that you learned in this chapter was most encouraging to you? _____
_____

As you conclude your study of 1 John, use Psalm 111:10 as the foundation of your closing prayer time.

A.C.T.S. PRAYER TIME

"The fear of the LORD is the beginning of wisdom; A good understanding have all those who do His commandments; His praise endures forever."
~ Psalm 111:10 NASB ~

A - *Adoration* _____

C - *Confession* _____

T - *Thanksgiving* _____

S - *Supplication* _____

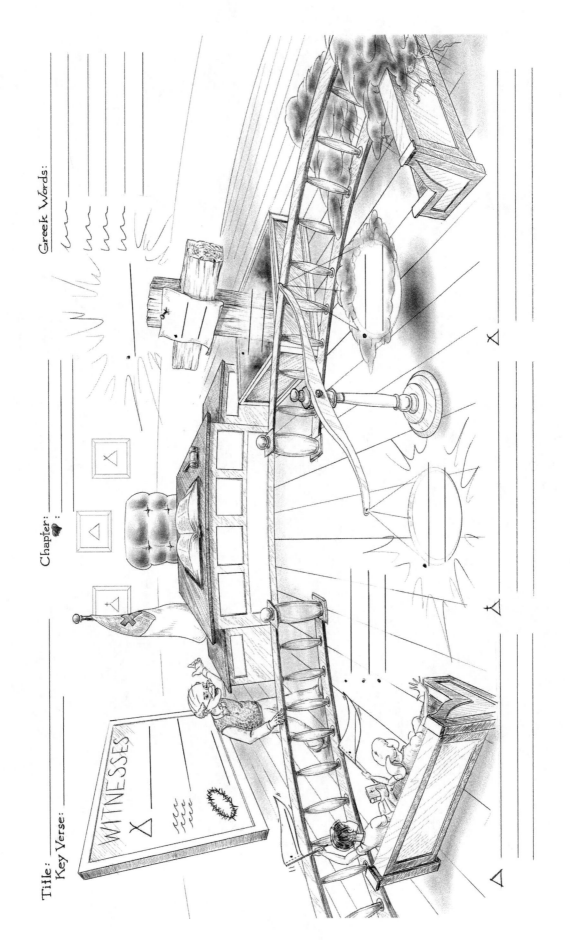

Title: _____

Key Verse: _____

Chapter: _____

Greek Words: _____

WITNESSES

307

CONGRATULATIONS!

Many times in life the end of one thing is the beginning of another.
We hope that will be true here. You have finished this study of 1 John,
but we hope that you will never finish studying the Bible.
The end of this study can be the beginning of the adventure of studying your
Bible for the rest of your life!

Our prayer for you is that you would …

"Have trusted Jesus for salvation.
Love deeply.
Obey faithfully.
Live righteously.
Know your God.
Be confident in your eternal life.
Fellowship daily with the Father, Son and His people.
May the peace of Christ be with you until we meet."

You are at the finish line of this race! Well done!

What book will you pick next?

WRITE!
MY COPY OF 1 JOHN

English	Greek Word	Further Definition	Page
Fellowship	koinonia	Partnership, communion, fellow traveler	

GOD
the Father

GOD
the Son

GOD
the Holy Spirit

GOD
the Father

GOD
the Son

GOD
the Holy Spirit

GOD
the Father

GOD
the Son

GOD
the Holy Spirit

GOD
the Father

GOD
the Son

GOD
the Holy Spirit

GOD
the Father

GOD
the Son

GOD
the Holy Spirit

GOD
the Father

GOD
the Son

GOD
the Holy Spirit

GOD
the Father

GOD
the Son

GOD
the Holy Spirit

GOD
the Father

GOD
the Son

GOD
the Holy Spirit

GOD
the Father

GOD
the Son

GOD
the Holy Spirit

GOD
the Father

GOD
the Son

GOD
the Holy Spirit

GOD
the Father

GOD
the Son

GOD
the Holy Spirit

GOD
the Father

GOD
the Son

GOD
the Holy Spirit

GOD
the Father

GOD
the Son

GOD
the Holy Spirit

GOD
the Father

GOD
the Son

GOD
the Holy Spirit

GOD
the Father

GOD
the Son

GOD
the Holy Spirit

GOD
the Father

GOD
the Son

GOD
the Holy Spirit

GOD
the Father

GOD
the Son

GOD
the Holy Spirit

GOD
the Father

GOD
the Son

GOD
the Holy Spirit

GOD
the Father

GOD
the Father

GOD
the Son

GOD
the Son

GOD
the Holy Spirit

GOD
the Holy Spirit

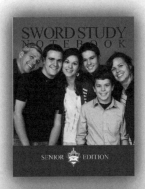
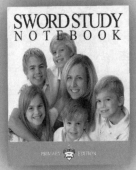

You Can Host

a Summer Bible Bee!

Encourage!
Recognize!
Reward!

FAMILY DISCIPLESHIP
(Cleverly Disguised as a Contest)

Everything you need is provided for three "Encouragement Parties" and the Local Celebration Day in August. Parents receive a Family Guide and each child gets his/her own age-appropriate, 20-minute per day Bible study on June 1st! Support local families as they discover a deeper walk with God through inductive Bible study and hiding His Word in their hearts!

Get details at www.BibleBee.org today!

Did you enjoy this study?

We Still Deliver!

There are three ways to continue your growth...

1. If you have children ages 7-18, join us next Summer for The National Bible Bee.

   - All materials delivered to you on June 1st.
   - Same inductive study method.
   - Same whole-family synchronized materials.
   - New Bible book to study each summer.
   - Meet like-minded families near you.
   - Win great prizes, with over $260,000 awarded at Nationals.

   Answer all your questions at www.BibleBee.org

2. If you just want the next study as soon as it is available,
   order it directly from The Shelby Kennedy Foundation at Store.BibleBee.org

3. Buy one of our other Sword Study titles at your local Christian bookstore.

www.SwordStudy.org | (937) 382-7250
www.BibleBee.org

 *The* SHELBY KENNEDY *Foundation*

ESV

Psalm 111:10

10 The fear of the LORD is the beginning of wisdom; all those who practice it have a good understanding. His praise endures forever!

Psalm 111:10

Week 1   ESV

John 8:12

12 Again Jesus spoke to them, saying, "I am the light of the world. Whoever follows me will not walk in darkness, but will have the light of life."

John 8:12

Week 2   ESV

1 John 1:3

3 that which we have seen and heard we proclaim also to you, so that you too may have fellowship with us; and indeed our fellowship is with the Father and with his Son Jesus Christ.

1 John 1:3

Week 3   ESV

Job 15:14-16

14 What is man, that he can be pure? Or he who is born of a woman, that he can be righteous? 15 Behold, God puts no trust in his holy ones, and the heavens are not pure in his sight; 16 how much less one who is abominable and corrupt, a man who drinks injustice like water!

Job 15:14-16

Week 4   ESV

Psalm 36:7-10

7 How precious is your steadfast love, O God! The children of mankind take refuge in the shadow of your wings. 8 They feast on the abundance of your house, and you give them drink from the river of your delights. 9 For with you is the fountain of life; in your light do we see light. 10 Oh, continue your steadfast love to those who know you, and your righteousness to the upright of heart!

Psalm 36:7-10

Week 5   ESV

Isaiah 43:1-2

1 But now thus says the LORD, he who created you, O Jacob, he who formed you, O Israel: "Fear not, for I have redeemed you; I have called you by name, you are mine. 2 When you pass through the waters, I will be with you; and through the rivers, they shall not overwhelm you; when you walk through fire you shall not be burned, and the flame shall not consume you.

Isaiah 43:1-2

Week 6   ESV

ESV

Jeremiah 9:23-24

23 Thus says the LORD: "Let not the wise man boast in his wisdom, let not the mighty man boast in his might, let not the rich man boast in his riches, 24 but let him who boasts boast in this, that he understands and knows me, that I am the LORD who practices steadfast love, justice, and righteousness in the earth. For in these things I delight, declares the LORD."

Jeremiah 9:23-24

Week 1   ESV

John 17:3

3 And this is eternal life, that they know you the only true God, and Jesus Christ whom you have sent.

John 17:3

Week 2   ESV

1 John 1:9

9 If we confess our sins, he is faithful and just to forgive us our sins and to cleanse us from all unrighteousness.

1 John 1:9

Week 3   ESV

Proverbs 28:13-14

13 Whoever conceals his transgressions will not prosper, but he who confesses and forsakes them will obtain mercy. 14 Blessed is the one who fears the LORD always, but whoever hardens his heart will fall into calamity.

Proverbs 28:13-14

Week 4   ESV

John 8:31-32

31 So Jesus said to the Jews who had believed him, "If you abide in my word, you are truly my disciples, 32 and you will know the truth, and the truth will set you free."

John 8:31-32

Week 5   ESV

2 Corinthians 6:16-18

16 What agreement has the temple of God with idols? For we are the temple of the living God; as God said, "I will make my dwelling among them and walk among them, and I will be their God, and they shall be my people.
17 Therefore go out from their midst, and be separate from them, says the Lord, and touch no unclean thing; then I will welcome you, 18 and I will be a father to you, and you shall be sons and daughters to me, says the Lord Almighty."

2 Corinthians 6:16-18

Week 6   ESV

ESV

Isaiah 45:22-23

22 "Turn to me and be saved, all the ends of the earth! For I am God, and there is no other. 23 By myself I have sworn; from my mouth has gone out in righteousness a word that shall not return: 'To me every knee shall bow, every tongue shall swear allegiance.'

Isaiah 45:22-23

Week 7   ESV

Philippians 3:8-11

8 Indeed, I count everything as loss because of the surpassing worth of knowing Christ Jesus my Lord. For his sake I have suffered the loss of all things and count them as rubbish, in order that I may gain Christ 9 and be found in him, not having a righteousness of my own that comes from the law, but that which comes through faith in Christ, the righteousness from God that depends on faith— 10 that I may know him and the power of his resurrection, and may share his sufferings, becoming like him in his death, 11 that by any means possible I may attain the resurrection from the dead.

Philippians 3:8-11

Week 8   ESV

2 Corinthians 5:14-15

14 For the love of Christ controls us, because we have concluded this: that one has died for all, therefore all have died; 15 and he died for all, that those who live might no longer live for themselves but for him who for their sake died and was raised.

2 Corinthians 5:14-15

Week 9   ESV

Psalm 119:160

160 The sum of your word is truth, and every one of your righteous rules endures forever.

Psalm 119:160

Week 10   ESV

Matthew 22:36-40

36 "Teacher, which is the great commandment in the Law?" 37 And he said to him, "You shall love the Lord your God with all your heart and with all your soul and with all your mind. 38 This is the great and first commandment. 39 And a second is like it: You shall love your neighbor as yourself. 40 On these two commandments depend all the Law and the Prophets."

Matthew 22:36-40

Week 11   ESV

Hosea 6:3-6

3 Let us know; let us press on to know the LORD; his going out is sure as the dawn; he will come to us as the showers, as the spring rains that water the earth." 4 What shall I do with you, O Ephraim? What shall I do with you, O Judah? Your love is like a morning cloud, like the dew that goes early away. 5 Therefore I have hewn them by the prophets; I have slain them by the words of my mouth, and my judgment goes forth as the light. 6 For I desire steadfast love and not sacrifice, the knowledge of God rather than burnt offerings.

Hosea 6:3-6

Week 12   ESV

1 John 4:7-10

7 Beloved, let us love one another, for love is from God, and whoever loves has been born of God and knows God. 8 Anyone who does not love does not know God, because God is love. 9 In this the love of God was made manifest among us, that God sent his only Son into the world, so that we might live through him. 10 In this is love, not that we have loved God but that he loved us and sent his Son to be the propitiation for our sins.

1 John 4:7-10

Week 8 ESV

2 Corinthians 5:20-21

20 Therefore, we are ambassadors for Christ, God making his appeal through us. We implore you on behalf of Christ, be reconciled to God. 21 For our sake he made him to be sin who knew no sin, so that in him we might become the righteousness of God.

2 Corinthians 5:20-21

Week 7 ESV

1 John 5:13

13 I write these things to you who believe in the name of the Son of God that you may know that you have eternal life.

1 John 5:13

Week 10 ESV

Ephesians 5:1-4

1 Therefore be imitators of God, as beloved children. 2 And walk in love, as Christ loved us and gave himself up for us, a fragrant offering and sacrifice to God. 3 But sexual immorality and all impurity or covetousness must not even be named among you, as is proper among saints. 4 Let there be no filthiness nor foolish talk nor crude joking, which are out of place, but instead let there be thanksgiving.

Ephesians 5:1-4

Week 9 ESV

Matthew 5:14-16

14 "You are the light of the world. A city set on a hill cannot be hidden. 15 Nor do people light a lamp and put it under a basket, but on a stand, and it gives light to all in the house. 16 In the same way, let your light shine before others, so that they may see your good works and give glory to your Father who is in heaven.

Matthew 5:14-16

Week 12 ESV

Acts 10:38-43

38 how God anointed Jesus of Nazareth with the Holy Spirit and with power. He went about doing good and healing all who were oppressed by the devil, for God was with him. 39 And we are witnesses of all that he did both in the country of the Jews and in Jerusalem. They put him to death by hanging him on a tree, 40 but God raised him on the third day and made him to appear, 41 not to all the people but to us who had been chosen by God as witnesses, who ate and drank with him after he rose from the dead. 42 And he commanded us to preach to the people and to testify that he is the one appointed by God to be judge of the living and the dead. 43 To him all the prophets bear witness that everyone who believes in him receives forgiveness of sins through his name."

Acts 10:38-43

Week 11 ESV

Psalm 111:10

10 The fear of the LORD is the beginning of wisdom: a good understanding have all they that do his commandments: his praise endureth for ever.

Psalm 111:10

Week 1   KJV

John 8:12

12 Then spake Jesus again unto them, saying, I am the light of the world: he that followeth me shall not walk in darkness, but shall have the light of life.

John 8:12

Week 2   KJV

1 John 1:3

3 That which we have seen and heard declare we unto you, that ye also may have fellowship with us: and truly our fellowship is with the Father, and with his Son Jesus Christ.

1 John 1:3

Week 3   KJV

Job 15:14-16

14 What is man, that he should be clean? and he which is born of a woman, that he should be righteous? 15 Behold, he putteth no trust in his saints; yea, the heavens are not clean in his sight. 16 How much more abominable and filthy is man, which drinketh iniquity like water?

Job 15:14-16

Week 4   KJV

Psalm 36:7-10

7 How excellent is thy lovingkindness, O God! therefore the children of men put their trust under the shadow of thy wings. 8 They shall be abundantly satisfied with the fatness of thy house; and thou shalt make them drink of the river of thy pleasures. 9 For with thee is the fountain of life: in thy light shall we see light. 10 O continue thy lovingkindness unto them that know thee; and thy righteousness to the upright in heart.

Psalm 36:7-10

Week 5   KJV

Isaiah 43:1-2

1 But now thus saith the LORD that created thee, O Jacob, and he that formed thee, O Israel, Fear not: for I have redeemed thee, I have called thee by thy name; thou art mine. 2 When thou passest through the waters, I will be with thee; and through the rivers, they shall not overflow thee: when thou walkest through the fire, thou shalt not be burned; neither shall the flame kindle upon thee.

Isaiah 43:1-2

Week 6   KJV

John 17:3

3 And this is life eternal, that they might know thee the only true God, and Jesus Christ, whom thou hast sent.

John 17:3

Week 2   KJV

Jeremiah 9:23-24

23 Thus saith the LORD, Let not the wise man glory in his wisdom, neither let the mighty man glory in his might, let not the rich man glory in his riches: 24 But let him that glorieth glory in this, that he understandeth and knoweth me, that I am the LORD which exercise lovingkindness, judgment, and righteousness, in the earth: for in these things I delight, saith the LORD.

Jeremiah 9:23-24

Week 1   KJV

Proverbs 28:13-14

13 He that covereth his sins shall not prosper: but whoso confesseth and forsaketh them shall have mercy. 14 Happy is the man that feareth always: but he that hardeneth his heart shall fall into mischief.

Proverbs 28:13-14

Week 4   KJV

1 John 1:9

9 If we confess our sins, he is faithful and just to forgive us our sins, and to cleanse us from all unrighteousness.

1 John 1:9

Week 3   KJV

2 Corinthians 6:16-18

16 And what agreement hath the temple of God with idols? for ye are the temple of the living God; as God hath said, I will dwell in them, and walk in them; and I will be their God, and they shall be my people. 17 Wherefore come out from among them, and be ye separate, saith the Lord, and touch not the unclean thing; and I will receive you, 18 And will be a Father unto you, and ye shall be my sons and daughters, saith the Lord Almighty.

2 Corinthians 6:16-18

Week 6   KJV

John 8:31-32

31 Then said Jesus to those Jews which believed on him, If ye continue in my word, then are ye my disciples indeed; 32 And ye shall know the truth, and the truth shall make you free.

John 8:31-32

Week 5   KJV

Isaiah 45:22-23

22 Look unto me, and be ye saved, all the ends of the earth: for I am God, and there is none else. 23 I have sworn by myself, the word is gone out of my mouth in righteousness, and shall not return, That unto me every knee shall bow, every tongue shall swear.

Isaiah 45:22-23

Week 7 KJV

Philippians 3:8-11

8 Yea doubtless, and I count all things but loss for the excellency of the knowledge of Christ Jesus my Lord: for whom I have suffered the loss of all things, and do count them but dung, that I may win Christ, 9 And be found in him, not having mine own righteousness, which is of the law, but that which is through the faith of Christ, the righteousness which is of God by faith: 10 That I may know him, and the power of his resurrection, and the fellowship of his sufferings, being made conformable unto his death; 11 If by any means I might attain unto the resurrection of the dead.

Philippians 3:8-11

Week 8   KJV

2 Corinthians 5:14-15

14 For the love of Christ constraineth us; because we thus judge, that if one died for all, then were all dead: 15 And that he died for all, that they which live should not henceforth live unto themselves, but unto him which died for them, and rose again.

2 Corinthians 5:14-15

Week 9   KJV

Psalm 119:160

160 Thy word is true from the beginning: and every one of thy righteous judgments endureth for ever.

Psalm 119:160

Week 10   KJV

Matthew 22:36-40

36 Master, which is the great commandment in the law? 37 Jesus said unto him, Thou shalt love the Lord thy God with all thy heart, and with all thy soul, and with all thy mind. 38 This is the first and great commandment. 39 And the second is like unto it, Thou shalt love thy neighbour as thyself. 40 On these two commandments hang all the law and the prophets.

Matthew 22:36-40

Week 11 KJV

Hosea 6:3-6

3 Then shall we know, if we follow on to know the LORD: his going forth is prepared as the morning; and he shall come unto us as the rain, as the latter and former rain unto the earth. 4 O Ephraim, what shall I do unto thee? O Judah, what shall I do unto thee? for your goodness is as a morning cloud, and as the early dew it goeth away. 5 Therefore have I hewed them by the prophets; I have slain them by the words of my mouth: and thy judgments are as the light that goeth forth. 6 For I desired mercy, and not sacrifice; and the knowledge of God more than burnt offerings.

Hosea 6:3-6

Week 12   KJV

1 John 4:7-10

7 Beloved, let us love one another: for love is of God; and every one that loveth is born of God, and knoweth God. 8 He that loveth not knoweth not God; for God is love. 9 In this was manifested the Love of God toward us, because that God sent his only begotten Son into the world, that we might live through him. 10 Herein is Love, not that we loved God, but that he loved us, and sent his Son To be the propitiation for our sins.

1 John 4:7-10

Week 8 KJV

2 Corinthians 5:20-21

20 Now then we are ambassadors for Christ, as though God did beseech you by us: we pray you in Christ's stead, be ye reconciled to God. 21 For he hath made him to be sin for us, who knew no sin; that we might be made the righteousness of God in him.

2 Corinthians 5:20-21

Week 7 KJV

1 John 5:13

13 These things have I written unto you that believe on the name of the Son of God; that ye may know that ye have eternal life, and that ye may believe on the name of the Son of God.

1 John 5:13

Week 10 KJV

Ephesians 5:1-4

1 Be ye therefore followers of God, as dear children;
2 And walk in love, as Christ also hath loved us, and hath given himself for us an offering and a sacrifice to God for a sweetsmelling savour. 3 But fornication, and all uncleanness, or covetousness, let it not be once named among you, as becometh saints; 4 Neither filthiness, nor foolish talking, nor jesting, which are not convenient: but rather giving of thanks.

Ephesians 5:1-4

Week 9 KJV

Matthew 5:14-16

14 Ye are the light of the world. A city that is set on an hill cannot be hid. 15 Neither do men light a candle, and put it under a bushel, but on a candlestick; and it giveth light unto all that are in the house. 16 Let your light so shine before men, that they may see your good works, and glorify your Father which is in heaven.

Matthew 5:14-16

Week 12 KJV

Acts 10:38-43

38 How God anointed Jesus of Nazareth with the Holy Ghost and with power: who went about doing good, and healing all that were oppressed of the devil; for God was with him. 39 And we are witnesses of all things which he did both in the land of the Jews, and in Jerusalem; whom they slew and hanged on a tree: 40 Him God raised up the third day, and showed him openly; 41 Not to all the people, but unto witnesses chosen before of God, even to us, who did eat and drink with him after he rose from the dead. 42 And he commanded us to preach unto the people, and to testify that it is he which was ordained of God to be the Judge of quick and dead. 43 To him give all the prophets witness, that through his name whosoever believeth in him shall receive remission of sins.

Acts 10:38-43

Week 11 KJV

Psalm 111:10

10 The fear of the LORD is the beginning of wisdom;
A good understanding have all those who do His
commandments; His praise endures forever.

Psalm 111:10

Week 1   NASB

John 8:12

12 Then Jesus again spoke to them, saying, " I am the
Light of the world; he who follows Me will not walk in the
darkness, but will have the Light of life."

John 8:12

Week 2   NASB

1 John 1:3

3 what we have seen and heard we proclaim to you also, so
that you too may have fellowship with us; and indeed our
fellowship is with the Father, and with His Son Jesus Christ.

1 John 1:3

Week 3   NASB

Job 15:14-16

14 "What is man, that he should be pure, Or he who is born
of a woman, that he should be righteous? 15 "Behold, He
puts no trust in His holy ones, And the heavens are not pure
in His sight; 16 How much less one who is detestable and
corrupt, Man, who drinks iniquity like water!

Job 15:14-16

Week 4   NASB

Psalm 36:7-10

7 How precious is Your lovingkindness, O God! And the
children of men take refuge in the shadow of Your wings. 8
They drink their fill of the abundance of Your house; And
You give them to drink of the river of Your delights. 9 For
with You is the fountain of life; In Your light we see light. 10
O continue Your lovingkindness to those who know You,
And Your righteousness to the upright in heart.

Psalm 36:7-10

Week 5   NASB

Isaiah 43:1-2

1 But now, thus says the LORD, your Creator, O Jacob,
And He who formed you, O Israel, "Do not fear, for I have
redeemed you; I have called you by name; you are Mine! 2
"When you pass through the waters, I will be with you; And
through the rivers, they will not overflow you. When you
walk through the fire, you will not be scorched, Nor will the
flame burn you.

Isaiah 43:1-2

Week 6   NASB

John 17:3

3 "This is eternal life, that they may know You, the only true God, and Jesus Christ whom You have sent.

John 17:3

Week 2   NASB

Jeremiah 9:23-24

3 Thus says the LORD, " Let not a wise man boast of his wisdom, and let not the mighty man boast of his might, let not a rich man boast of his riches; 24 but let him who boasts boast of this, that he understands and knows Me, that I am the LORD who exercises lovingkindness, justice and righteousness on earth; for I delight in these things," declares the LORD.

Jeremiah 9:23-24

Week 1   NASB

Proverbs 28:13-14

3 He who conceals his transgressions will not prosper, But he who confesses and forsakes them will find compassion. 14 How blessed is the man who fears always, But he who hardens his heart will fall into calamity.

Proverbs 28:13-14

Week 4   NASB

1 John 1:9

9 If we confess our sins, He is faithful and righteous to forgive us our sins and to cleanse us from all unrighteousness.

1 John 1:9

Week 3   NASB

2 Corinthians 6:16-18

16 Or what agreement has the temple of God with idols? For we are the temple of the living God; just as God said, " I WILL DWELL IN THEM AND WALK AMONG THEM; AND I WILL BE THEIR GOD, AND THEY SHALL BE MY PEOPLE. 17 " Therefore, COME OUT FROM THEIR MIDST AND BE SEPARATE," says the Lord. "AND DO NOT TOUCH WHAT IS UNCLEAN; And I will welcome you. 18 " And I will be a father to you, And you shall be sons and daughters to Me," Says the Lord Almighty.

2 Corinthians 6:16-18

Week 6   NASB

John 8:31-32

31 So Jesus was saying to those Jews who had believed Him, " If you continue in My word, then you are truly disciples of Mine; 32 and you will know the truth, and the truth will make you free."

John 8:31-32

Week 5   NASB

NASB

Isaiah 45:22-23

22 " Turn to Me and be saved, all the ends of the earth; For I am God, and there is no other. 23 " I have sworn by Myself, The word has gone forth from My mouth in righteousness And will not turn back, That to Me every knee will bow, every tongue will swear allegiance.

Isaiah 45:22-23

Week 7 NASB

Philippians 3:8-11

8 More than that, I count all things to be loss in view of the surpassing value of knowing Christ Jesus my Lord, for whom I have suffered the loss of all things, and count them but rubbish so that I may gain Christ, 9 and may be found in Him, not having a righteousness of my own derived from the Law, but that which is through faith in Christ, the righteousness which comes from God on the basis of faith, 10 that I may know Him and the power of His resurrection and the fellowship of His sufferings, being conformed to His death; 11 in order that I may attain to the resurrection from the dead.

Philippians 3:8-11

Week 8   NASB

2 Corinthians 5:14-15

14 For the love of Christ controls us, having concluded this, that one died for all, therefore all died; 15 and He died for all, so that they who live might no longer live for themselves, but for Him who died and rose again on their behalf.

2 Corinthians 5:14-15

Week 9 NASB

Psalm 119:160

160 The sum of Your word is truth, And every one of Your righteous ordinances is everlasting.

Psalm 119:160

Week 10   NASB

Matthew 22:36-40

36 "Teacher, which is the great commandment in the Law?" 37 And He said to him, " ' YOU SHALL LOVE THE LORD YOUR GOD WITH ALL YOUR HEART, AND WITH ALL YOUR SOUL, AND WITH ALL YOUR MIND.' 38 "This is the great and foremost commandment. 39 "The second is like it, 'YOU SHALL LOVE YOUR NEIGHBOR AS YOURSELF.' 40 "On these two commandments depend the whole Law and the Prophets."

Matthew 22:36-40

Week 11 NASB

Hosea 6:3-6

3 "So let us know, let us press on to know the LORD. His going forth is as certain as the dawn; And He will come to us like the rain, Like the spring rain watering the earth." 4 What shall I do with you, O Ephraim? What shall I do with you, O Judah? For your loyalty is like a morning cloud And like the dew which goes away early. 5 Therefore I have hewn them in pieces by the prophets; I have slain them by the words of My mouth; And the judgments on you are like the light that goes forth. 6 For I delight in loyalty rather than sacrifice, And in the knowledge of God rather than burnt offerings.

Hosea 6:3-6

Week 12   NASB

1 John 4:7-10

7 Beloved, let us love one another, for love is from God; and everyone who loves is born of God and knows God. 8 The one who does not love does not know God, for God is love. 9 By this the love of God was manifested in us, that God has sent His only begotten Son into the world so that we might live through Him. 10 In this is love, not that we loved God, but that He loved us and sent His Son to be the propitiation for our sins.

1 John 4:7-10

Week 8 NASB

2 Corinthians 5:20-21

20 Therefore, we are ambassadors for Christ, as though God were making an appeal through us; we beg you on behalf of Christ, be reconciled to God. 21 He made Him who knew no sin to be sin on our behalf, so that we might become the righteousness of God in Him.

2 Corinthians 5:20-21

Week 7   NASB

1 John 5:13

13 These things I have written to you who believe in the name of the Son of God, so that you may know that you have eternal life.

1 John 5:13

Week 10 NASB

Ephesians 5:1-4

1 Therefore be imitators of God, as beloved children; 2 and walk in love, just as Christ also loved you and gave Himself up for us, an offering and a sacrifice to God as a fragrant aroma. 3 But immorality or any impurity or greed must not even be named among you, as is proper among saints; 4 and there must be no filthiness and silly talk, or coarse jesting, which are not fitting, but rather giving of thanks.

Ephesians 5:1-4

Week 9   NASB

Matthew 5:14-16

14 "You are the light of the world. A city set on a hill cannot be hidden; 15 nor does anyone light a lamp and put it under a basket, but on the lampstand, and it gives light to all who are in the house. 16 "Let your light shine before men in such a way that they may see your good works, and glorify your Father who is in heaven.

Matthew 5:14-16

Week 12 NASB

Acts 10:38-43

38 "You know of Jesus of Nazareth, how God anointed Him with the Holy Spirit and with power, and how He went about doing good and healing all who were oppressed by the devil, for God was with Him. 39 "We are witnesses of all the things He did both in the land of the Jews and in Jerusalem. They also put Him to death by hanging Him on a cross. 40 "God raised Him up on the third day and granted that He become visible, 41 not to all the people, but to witnesses who were chosen beforehand by God, that is, to us who ate and drank with Him after He arose from the dead. 42 "And He ordered us to preach to the people, and solemnly to testify that this is the One who has been appointed by God as Judge of the living and the dead. 43 Of Him all the prophets bear witness that through His name everyone who believes in Him receives forgiveness of sins."

Acts 10:38-43

Week 11   NASB

NKJV

Psalm 111:10

10 The fear of the LORD is the beginning of wisdom;
A good understanding have all those who do His
commandments. His praise endures forever.

Psalm 111:10

Week 1 NKJV

John 8:12

12 Then Jesus spoke to them again, saying, "I am the light
of the world. He who follows Me shall not walk in darkness,
but have the light of life."

John 8:12

Week 2   NKJV

1 John 1:3

3 that which we have seen and heard we declare to you,
that you also may have fellowship with us; and truly
our fellowship is with the Father and with His Son
Jesus Christ.

1 John 1:3

Week 3 NKJV

Job 15:14-16

14 "What is man, that he could be pure? And he who is
born of a woman, that he could be righteous? 15 If God puts
no trust in His saints, And the heavens are not pure in His
sight, 16 How much less man, who is abominable and filthy,
Who drinks iniquity like water!

Job 15:14-16

Week 4   NKJV

Psalm 36:7-10

7 How precious is Your lovingkindness, O God!
Therefore the children of men put their trust under the
shadow of Your wings. 8 They are abundantly satisfied
with the fullness of Your house, And You give them
drink from the river of Your pleasures. 9 For with You
is the fountain of life; In Your light we see light. 10 Oh,
continue Your lovingkindness to those who know You,
And Your righteousness to the upright in heart.

Psalm 36:7-10

Week 5   NKJV

Isaiah 43:1-2

1 But now, thus says the LORD, who created you, O Jacob,
And He who formed you, O Israel: "Fear not, for I have
redeemed you; I have called you by your name; You are
Mine. 2 When you pass through the waters, I will be with
you; And through the rivers, they shall not overflow you.
When you walk through the fire, you shall not be burned,
Nor shall the flame scorch you.

Isaiah 43:1-2

Week 6   NKJV

John 17:3

3 And this is eternal life, that they may know You, the only true God, and Jesus Christ whom You have sent.

John 17:3

Week 2   NKJV

Jeremiah 9:23-24

23 Thus says the LORD: "Let not the wise man glory in his wisdom, Let not the mighty man glory in his might, Nor let the rich man glory in his riches; 24 But let him who glories glory in this, That he understands and knows Me, That I am the LORD, exercising lovingkindness, judgment, and righteousness in the earth. For in these I delight," says the LORD.

Jeremiah 9:23-24

Week 1   NKJV

Proverbs 28:13-14

13 He who covers his sins will not prosper, But whoever confesses and forsakes them will have mercy. 14 Happy is the man who is always reverent, But he who hardens his heart will fall into calamity.

Proverbs 28:13-14

Week 4   NKJV

1 John 1:9

9 If we confess our sins, He is faithful and just to forgive us our sins and to cleanse us from all unrighteousness.

1 John 1:9

Week 3   NKJV

2 Corinthians 6:16-18

16 And what agreement has the temple of God with idols? For you are the temple of the living God. As God has said: "I will dwell in them And walk among them. I will be their God, And they shall be My people." 17 Therefore "Come out from among them And be separate, says the Lord. Do not touch what is unclean, And I will receive you." 18 "I will be a Father to you, And you shall be My sons and daughters, Says the LORD Almighty."

2 Corinthians 6:16-18

Week 6   NKJV

John 8:31-32

31 Then Jesus said to those Jews who believed Him, "If you abide in My word, you are My disciples indeed. 32 And you shall know the truth, and the truth shall make you free."

John 8:31-32

Week 5   NKJV

Isaiah 45:22-23

22 "Look to Me, and be saved, All you ends of the earth! For I am God, and there is no other. 23 I have sworn by Myself; The word has gone out of My mouth in righteousness, And shall not return, That to Me every knee shall bow, Every tongue shall take an oath.

Isaiah 45:22-23

Week 7 NKJV

Philippians 3:8-11

8 Yet indeed I also count all things loss for the excellence of the knowledge of Christ Jesus my Lord, for whom I have suffered the loss of all things, and count them as rubbish, that I may gain Christ 9 and be found in Him, not having my own righteousness, which is from the law, but that which is through faith in Christ, the righteousness which is from God by faith; 10 that I may know Him and the power of His resurrection, and the fellowship of His sufferings, being conformed to His death, 11 if, by any means, I may attain to the resurrection from the dead.

Philippians 3:8-11

Week 8   NKJV

2 Corinthians 5:14-15

14 For the love of Christ compels us, because we judge thus: that if One died for all, then all died; 15 and He died for all, that those who live should live no longer for themselves, but for Him who died for them and rose again.

2 Corinthians 5:14-15

Week 9   NKJV

Psalm 119:160

160 The entirety of Your word is truth, And every one of Your righteous judgments endures forever.

Psalm 119:160

Week 10   NKJV

Matthew 22:36-40

36 "Teacher, which is the great commandment in the law?" 37 Jesus said to him, ""You shall love the LORD your God with all your heart, with all your soul, and with all your mind.' 38 This is the first and great commandment. 39 And the second is like it: "You shall love your neighbor as yourself.' 40 On these two commandments hang all the Law and the Prophets."

Matthew 22:36-40

Week 11 NKJV

Hosea 6:3-6

3 Let us know, Let us pursue the knowledge of the LORD. His going forth is established as the morning; He will come to us like the rain, Like the latter and former rain to the earth. 4 "O Ephraim, what shall I do to you? O Judah, what shall I do to you? For your faithfulness is like a morning cloud, And like the early dew it goes away. 5 Therefore I have hewn them by the prophets, I have slain them by the words of My mouth; And your judgments are like light that goes forth. 6 For I desire mercy and not sacrifice, And the knowledge of God more than burnt offerings.

Hosea 6:3-6

Week 12   NKJV

NKJV

1 John 4:7-10

7 Beloved, let us love one another, for love is of God; and everyone who loves is born of God and knows God. 8 He who does not love does not know God, for God is love. 9 In this the love of God was manifested toward us, that God has sent His only begotten Son into the world, that we might live through Him. 10 In this is love, not that we loved God, but that He loved us and sent His Son to be the propitiation for our sins.

1 John 4:7-10

Week 8 NKJV

2 Corinthians 5:20-21

20 Now then, we are ambassadors for Christ, as though God were pleading through us: we implore you on Christ's behalf, be reconciled to God. 21 For He made Him who knew no sin to be sin for us, that we might become the righteousness of God in Him.

2 Corinthians 5:20-21

Week 7 NKJV

1 John 5:13

13 These things I have written to you who believe in the name of the Son of God, that you may know that you have eternal life, and that you may continue to believe in the name of the Son of God.

1 John 5:13

Week 10 NKJV

Ephesians 5:1-4

1 Therefore be imitators of God as dear children. 2 And walk in love, as Christ also has loved us and given Himself for us, an offering and a sacrifice to God for a sweet-smelling aroma. 3 But fornication and all uncleanness or covetousness, let it not even be named among you, as is fitting for saints; 4 neither filthiness, nor foolish talking, nor coarse jesting, which are not fitting, but rather giving of thanks.

Ephesians 5:1-4

Week 9 NKJV

Matthew 5:14-16

14 "You are the light of the world. A city that is set on a hill cannot be hidden. 15 Nor do they light a lamp and put it under a basket, but on a lampstand, and it gives light to all who are in the house. 16 Let your light so shine before men, that they may see your good works and glorify your Father in heaven.

Matthew 5:14-16

Week 12 NKJV

Acts 10:38-43

38 how God anointed Jesus of Nazareth with the Holy Spirit and with power, who went about doing good and healing all who were oppressed by the devil, for God was with Him. 39 And we are witnesses of all things which He did both in the land of the Jews and in Jerusalem, whom they killed by hanging on a tree. 40 Him God raised up on the third day, and showed Him openly, 41 not to all the people, but to witnesses chosen before by God, even to us who ate and drank with Him after He arose from the dead. 42 And He commanded us to preach to the people, and to testify that it is He who was ordained by God to be Judge of the living and the dead. 43 To Him all the prophets witness that, through His name, whoever believes in Him will receive remission of sins.

Acts 10:38-43

Week 11 NKJV